STEAM WHALING IN THE WESTERN ARCTIC

Herschel Island in 1893-1894

John Bertonccini (1872-1947)

Old Dartmouth Historical Society, gift of Mr. and Mrs.
Eliot D. Stetson, Jr., 1971

Steam Whaling in the Western Arctic

JOHN R. BOCKSTOCE

with contributions
by William A. Baker
and Charles F. Batchelder

Published at the New Bedford Whaling Museum
by the Old Dartmouth Historical Society
New Bedford, Massachusetts
1977

Whaleboats cruising in young ice near Point Barrow, 1912
photograph courtesy of the American Geographical Society

CONTENTS

Many people have helped with the preparation of this catalogue and exhibition, and I wish to thank them for their generous assistance throughout the past year. I am especially indebted to Dr. Thomas Norton, Mr. Gale Huntington, and Mrs. Dorothy Cottle Poole of the Dukes County Historical Society; Dr. Kenneth R. Martin of the Kendall Whaling Museum; Mrs. Virginia Adams, Providence Public Library; Mr. Stuart C. Sherman, John Hay Library, Brown University; Mr. Philip C. F. Smith, Peabody Museum of Salem; Mr. Albert M. Barnes, The Mariners Museum; Mr. Douglass C. Fonda, Jr., International Marine Archives; Mr. Bruce Barnes, New Bedford Free Public Library; Mrs. Erica Parmi, Stefansson Collection, Dartmouth College; Mr. Karl Kortum, San Francisco Maritime Museum; Dr. Paul McCarthy, University of Alaska Archives; Dr. Melvin H. Jackson, Museum of History and Technology, Smithsonian Institution; Miss M. K. Swingle, California Historical Society; Mr. Thomas B. Crowley, Crowley Maritime Corporation; and Dr. Paul Fenimore Cooper, Jr., Mr. Richard Finnie, Mrs. Flavel Gifford, Captain Harold Huycke, Mrs. Barbara Johnson, Mr. Bernhard Kilian, Mr. Francis B. Lothrop, Mrs. Louvetta Bertonccini, and the descendants of Edward Avery McIlhenny. Logistical support near Point Barrow, Alaska, was provided by the U.S. Naval Arctic Research Laboratory.

Finally, I would like to thank Mr. Philip F. Purrington, Senior Curator of the Old Dartmouth Historical Society, whose broad and profound understanding of the history of the American whale fishery has contributed significantly to my research; I deeply appreciate his unselfish advice and useful criticisms. Similarly Mr. Richard C. Kugler, Director, has constantly encouraged this project and offered his every assistance. I am very grateful for his help.

J. R. B.
New Bedford, Massachusetts
December 1976

INTRODUCTION

In the thirty years from 1880 to 1910, the American whalemen concentrated their efforts on pursuing the bowhead whale in the waters north of Bering Strait. A highly specialized endeavor, almost every aspect of the hunt was determined by one basic, inescapable fact: in the western Arctic, ice was seldom absent. The schedule of voyages, the gear and implements for taking whales, the clothing and rations for the crews, the vessels themselves—all were designed or altered for survival and effective use in a harsh, ice-bound climate. Of the adaptations that sustained the bowhead fishery, the use of steam as an auxiliary source of power for the whaleship was the most radical departure from previous practice.

Neither the idea nor the actual use of steam power on whaleships was new in 1879, when *Mary and Helen*, the first of the American steam whalers, was launched. Twenty years earlier, British whalemen had built the prototypes, *Narwhal* and *Dundee*, and so great did they find the advantages of steam in the Greenland fishery that the construction of new vessels and the conversion of old ones proceeded rapidly. By 1865, their sailing whaleships were obsolete.

In Norway, experiments with steam were also underway. In 1863, Svend Foyn, an inventive whaling merchant, launched *Spes & Fides,* the first of the steam-powered catcher boats. Foyn's new craft not only adapted steam to the actual hunt for whales; it provided a stable platform that permitted the use of his other important invention, the large, explosive, cannon-fired harpoon. Together, the catcher boat and the large harpoon ushered in the technology of modern whale hunting, although their widespread use awaited the opening of the rich Antarctic whaling grounds. In 1909, as the American Arctic fishery expired, the Norwegians entered the south polar regions in force, bringing seventeen catcher boats and seven factory ships to operate from a base on South Georgia Island. The era of modern whaling had begun and the long American dominance of the fishery was over.

For the Americans, there was little incentive to use steam power until the declining number of bowhead whales forced the whalemen to extend their search farther and farther into the Arctic. Only then could they justify the extra costs of power plants and the coal to fuel them. The tremendous success of *Mary and Helen's* maiden voyage resolved their calculations in a compelling way and led to the construction of ten steamers like her, all bark-rigged, strongly built, handsome vessels. Twelve other vessels—older whaleships or onetime merchantmen—were converted to auxiliary steam power, but unlike the British, the Americans never entirely gave up on the sailing whalers. Such well-known veterans of the fleet as *Alice Knowles, Andrew Hicks, Charles W. Morgan* and *Wanderer,* worked the Arctic bowhead grounds along with the steamers, but with increasing disadvantage. By 1906, they and most of the sailing whaleships that survived returned to New Bedford to finish out their days as sperm whalers in more temperate waters and kinder climates.

The characteristics of the steam whalers and the history of their employment are the subjects of this publication, which is issued with a twofold purpose. It is meant to serve as a catalogue for a special exhibition at the Whaling Museum on "The Age of Steam Whaling in the Western Arctic," and to stand thereafter as a permanent contribution to knowledge about this last significant phase of American whaling history. The Museum's Curator of Ethnology, John R. Bockstoce, has undertaken the organization of the exhibition and the preparation of the publication, bringing to both tasks a scholar's familiarity with the records of the fishery and ten seasons of field experience on the land and water where its history was enacted. In a separate essay, William A. Baker, Curator of the Francis R. Hart Nautical Museum of Massachusetts Institute of Technology, applies the expertise of a naval architect to the design and construction of the class of vessels built for that enterprise. To illustrate their essays, a generous selection of photographs taken in the Arctic at the time provides a rare picture of one of the most adventuresome chapters in America's maritime history.

Richard C. Kugler, Director
The Old Dartmouth Historical Society
and Whaling Museum

WM. LEWIS

Importer of Whale Bone and Oil,

13 Hamilton
Street.

P. O. Box 66.

New Bedford, Mass., Nr. 21 188

Steam Whaling in the Western Arctic

John R. Bockstoce

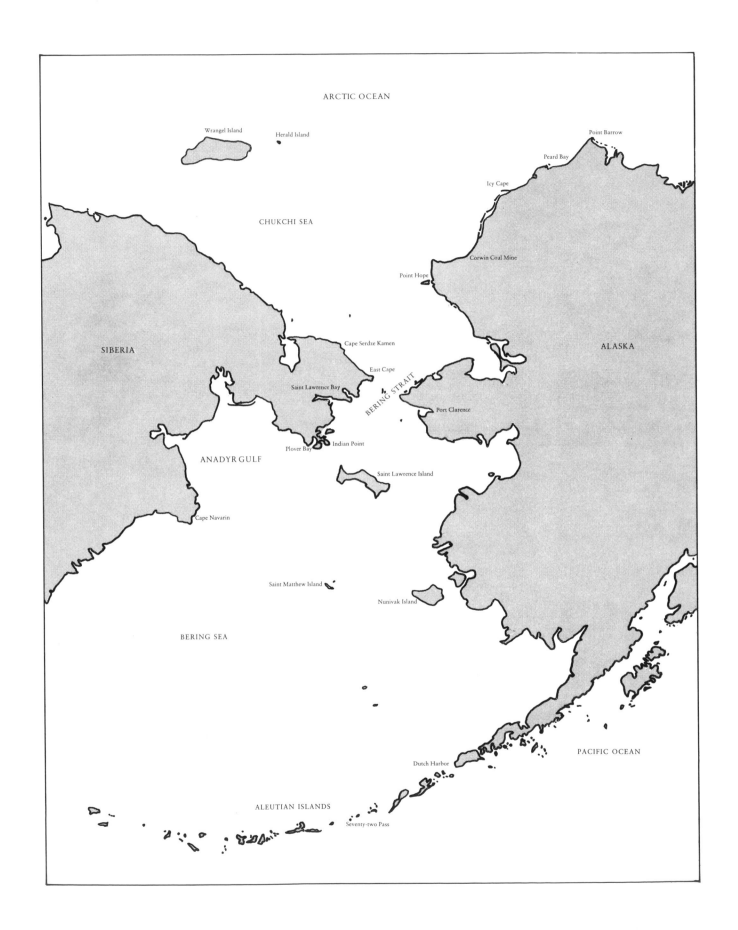

ARCTIC OCEAN

Wrangel Island

Herald Island

Point Barrow

Peard Bay

Icy Cape

CHUKCHI SEA

Corwin Coal Mine

Point Hope

SIBERIA

Cape Serdze Kamen

ALASKA

East Cape

Saint Lawrence Bay

BERING STRAIT

Port Clarence

Indian Point

Plover Bay

ANADYR GULF

Saint Lawrence Island

Cape Navarin

Saint Matthew Island

Nunivak Island

BERING SEA

PACIFIC OCEAN

Dutch Harbor

ALEUTIAN ISLANDS

Seventy-two Pass

THE VOYAGE OF THE *POLAR BEAR*

On August 13, 1914, the little gasoline whaling schooner *Polar Bear* was sailing slowly up the southwest coast of Banks Island in the Canadian Arctic, about fifteen miles from shore. The men on deck, adjusting to the roll from the long greasy swell coming in from the northwest, were glad to be on the lookout for whales. They had been trapped by the ice the previous September as they were on their way out of the Arctic and had spent the next eleven months frozen in near Barter Island, Alaska, four hundred miles from their present position.

Standing out from the anxious bustle of the younger crewmen were two officers, men in their sixties who moved easily in their parkas and mukluks with the economical actions of those long experienced in their trade. As they arranged the gear in their whaleboats, hung in davits on either side of the schooner, Billy Mogg, first mate, and Bill Seymour, second mate, could well have reflected on long years of service that spanned nearly the whole era of steam whaling in the western Arctic. Their careers, like that enterprise itself, had flowered and withered. Mogg's in particular had flourished and declined with the industry. Thirty years earlier, as a young Cornishman, he had sailed as a boatsteerer, or harpooneer, on *Mary and Helen II*, one of the early steam whalers. He had been a shore whaler at the Pacific Steam Whaling Company's station at Point Barrow, Alaska, and later was one of the Company's most successful officers on the astoundingly profitable voyage of the *Mary D. Hume*. Spending most of the 1890's aboard whalers wintering in the Arctic, it was not until 1901 that he took charge of a vessel, the small schooner *Altair*. His luck, however, declined in the first decade of the twentieth century, and he lost two vessels in shipwrecks. By 1910, with bowheads scarce and their baleen losing value rapidly, he again shipped as an officer, or occasionally as an ice pilot, on trading and freighting vessels.

The men aboard *Polar Bear* knew that if the whaling industry was not yet dead, then it was dying quickly and that the market for baleen, commonly known as whalebone, was limited and very soft. Most of the voyages' profits had already been made through trade with the Eskimos for furs, but they were determined to try for a little more.

As the schooner moved quietly through the scattered ice, Mogg and Seymour, together with Sam Brown and Napasak—Eskimo harpooneers signed on at Indian Point and East Cape, Siberia—watched carefully for the V-shaped vapor spout of the bowhead. They had seen few whales on the grounds near Cape Bathurst and now hoped to find them near Banks Island. Captain Louis Lane had agreed to go there because his trading operations were nearly finished for the cruise.

Suddenly Napasak shouted, pointing off the port side, and there, hanging momentarily in the shimmering Arctic mirage, was the puffy ball of vapor. Within seconds the sound carried down to them, the PAHHHH, PAHHHH of air exhausting from the huge lungs of two whales. Seymour and Mogg immediately jumped for their whaleboats, lowering away as their crews piled in after them. Quickly rigging the masts, they had sails up and began running down the half mile separating them from the whales. The bowheads had taken their usual four or five breaths before submerging and traveling on, so Mogg and Seymour aimed their boats about four hundred yards beyond, hoping to reach the point before the whales surfaced again. They judged well, for within fifteen minutes the bowheads rose not twenty yards from Seymour's boat. Mogg and Seymour had already quietly switched from the rudder to a long steering oar, which made the boat far more maneuverable at close quarters, and Seymour leaned hard on his, bringing the bow in line with the direction of the ripply turbulence that indicated a whale was not far from the surface. From the whale's blind spot, directly behind it, he was ready to run onto the animal.

By this time Napasak in the bow had pulled the safe pins from the darting guns and tested to see that the first few fathoms of the harpoon line were clear. The harpoon's toggle iron was mounted in lugs at the end of the shaft, alongside the darting gun and so arranged that when the whale was struck, a small bomb would simultaneously be fired, timed to explode a few seconds later and thereby kill the creature quickly.

As the whale rose to blow a second time, Seymour brought the bow of the boat within a few feet of its shiny black back,

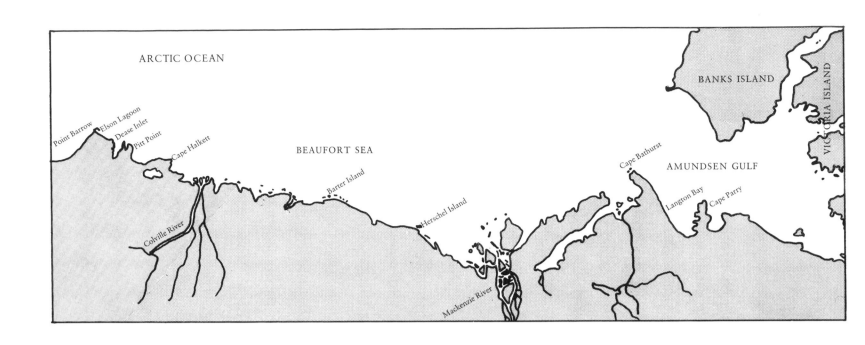

ARCTIC OCEAN

BANKS ISLAND

VICTORIA ISLAND

Point Barrow
Elson Lagoon
Dease Inlet
Pitt Point
Cape Halkett

BEAUFORT SEA

Barter Island

Colville River

Herschel Island

Mackenzie River

Cape Bathurst

AMUNDSEN GULF

Langton Bay
Cape Parry

Mogg's boat underway
photograph courtesy of Bernhard Kilian

Mogg's boat securing Seymour's whale
Old Dartmouth Historical Society

and Napasak, leaning far over the gunwale, shoved the iron deeply into the depression behind the blow holes, which marked the base of its skull. The toggle head of the iron, razor sharp, cut through the thick skin and Napasak felt the increasing resistance as it passed through the wide layer of blubber and entered the muscle below. Finally it sunk deep enough to trip the trigger rod of the darting gun, setting off the charge with a roar, driving the bomb past the toggle iron, deep into the whale, and blowing the harpoon shaft back into the air past the Eskimo's outstretched arm, now buried to the elbow in the water from the extension of his thrust.

Instantly the whale threw its twelve-foot flukes into the air, crashing them into the boat and showing the crew that he would dive to escape rather than run on the surface. Napasak, still in the bow, jumped nimbly aside as the harpoon line twanged taut and began to run from the line tubs, aft around the loggerhead and then forward through the bow chocks, smoking as it went. The crew quickly dropped the mast as the boat gained forward motion, and all gear, paddles and oars were placed out of the line's way. In the midst of this commotion, eight seconds after Napasak struck the whale, the men felt the dull WHUMP of the exploding bomb through their mukluks on the boat's hull.

Seymour quickly shipped the long steering oar and scrambled over the thwarts, avoiding the men and the line,

to change places with Napasak, who moved to the stern. Once the boatsteerer harpooned the whale, the officer's duty was to kill it. In earlier days, he did so by striking the whale with a long lance, pumping the blade in and out through the ribs to strike a vital organ. After 1870, with the perfection of the bomb gun, he could do so more easily by firing a bomb similar to the darting gun's into the whale from a thirty-five pound brass shoulder gun.

More than 150 fathoms of line had run out of the tubs when Seymour, sensing that the whale would surface soon, bent to take the shoulder gun from its wooden box near the bow. As he did, the line, still whirring from the tubs, picked up a kink that thudded around the loggerhead, then jammed hard in the bow chocks. The boat, now directly pulled by the fifty-ton whale, instantly picked up speed and began to tilt forward, being pulled under by the jammed line. As the stern began to rise out of the water, Seymour groped for the hatchet stored under the gunwale to cut the line. The boat began to tilt precariously, and realizing he was too late, Seymour managed to climb over the rolling hull as it capsized, throwing the rest of the crew into the icy water.

Mogg's boat, not far away, veered to pick the men up. At the same moment, the whale broke the surface milling and thrashing in a death flurry. Mogg, now in the bow, fired a bomb from his shoulder gun into the base of the whale's skull, severing the spinal cord and killing it instantly. Nearby,

Righting Seymour's boat
photograph courtesy of Bernhard Kilian

Captain Lane in *Polar Bear* signaled to the young engineer, Ben Kilian, for power and brought the schooner to the boats to fish the men from the water. *Polar Bear* had been close to the scene because Lane knew that the harpooned whale might try to run for the safety of the pack and had taken the schooner—with the motor running to frighten the animal—between it and the ice.

As soon as the capsized boat had been righted, the crew set about cutting in the whale. The cutting stage, a three-plank platform suspended from the side of the schooner, was lowered and the cutting tackle—the heavy blocks and falls for hoisting blubber and baleen—was rigged between the masts. With Mogg in charge, a series of parallel cuts were first made in the whale's blubber to permit the removal of the heavy blanket pieces, which were taken, not for oil as in former years, but to feed the Eskimo crewmen, who considered it a delicacy.

The crew then turned to taking the baleen. A line was first looped around the upper jaw and while the men, aided by the winch, maintained tension on it, Sam Brown was lowered onto the whale with an axe to cut through the enormous skull. Slowly, as Brown's chopping freed it, the two-thousand-pound piece rose from the pull of the tackle and was brought over the gunwale and lowered on deck. The slabs of baleen were cut from the jawbone with cutting spades, then stored in the hold for cleaning and washing later.[1]

In this way was enacted one of the last scenes of the western Arctic whale fishery. The baleen from the voyage was sold in a market that paid less than one-tenth of its value a decade earlier. For *Polar Bear*, it was her last whaling voyage, and she herself was the last vessel to be entered in the western Arctic fishery. For the next decade whales would occasionally be taken and ships would clear port on whaling voyages, but whale products had little value and a customs clearance for whaling was often only a convenient way of registering a vessel bound for a trading or freighting voyage.

Curiously enough, the conditions that killed the western Arctic fishery were similar to those that in the 1870's had brought about the age of the steam whalers, and with them, the greatest innovative surge in the history of the American whaling industry.

Cutting in on *Polar Bear*
photograph courtesy of Bernhard Kilian

Hoisting the blanket piece
photograph courtesy of Bernhard Kilian

Chopping out the headbone
Old Dartmouth Historical Society

Sam Brown, on the whale with a rope around his waist, leans against crossed cutting spades while chopping through the whale's skull to free the headbone. On the cutting stage are Billy Mogg (right) and Captain Louis Lane (left) in front of Bill Seymour.

Lowering the headbone on deck
photograph courtesy of the University of Alaska Archives
Billy Mogg directs the lowering of the headbone. The plates of baleen in the whale's upper jaw serve to filter plankton from the water.

The whaling grounds of Bering Strait and the Arctic Ocean were discovered in 1848 and rapidly became the most productive source of whale products in the industry. They remained so for more than sixty years because of the great numbers of bowhead whales (*Balaena mysticetus*) found there. These large, docile, slow-moving creatures were found in dense concentrations, were easily taken, and were exceptionally profitable, yielding on an average one hundred barrels of oil and fifteen hundred pounds of baleen per animal. The oil was sold primarily for illumination and the baleen was made into corset stays, skirt hoops, and buggy whips. Flexible and resilient, baleen was the only material available in the nineteenth century that approximated the properties supplied by spring steel, celluloid and flexible plastics in the twentieth. After the Civil War, when its major user, the fashion industry, came to require more and more of the substance, and the price of baleen rose accordingly, the whaling industry turned increasingly to the bowhead fishery of the North Pacific and Arctic.

Before 1865, when whale oil prices remained comparatively high, the April-to-October Arctic season generally yielded regular profits. Between 1865 and 1876 a series of misfortunes caused those profits to slump dramatically. First among them was the heavy loss of vessels in the Arctic fleet. In 1865 the Confederate raider *Shenandoah* burned twenty-one whaleships near Bering Strait and caused the wreck of another. In 1871 thirty-two were abandoned in the ice on the northwestern coast of Alaska; in 1876 twelve more succumbed to the same cause, and at least ten others were lost in the Arctic in that twelve-year period, making a total of seventy-six vessels, or an average of more than six a year, destroyed by ice or war. Combined with these losses was the vigorous penetration of the whale-oil market by petroleum products, natural gas, and vegetable oils. The petroleum industry, stimulated by the war, quickly established distribution and marketing methods which soon cut heavily into the demand for whale oils.

By 1875 the outlook for the industry was not good. Whale oil was selling at only 65¼¢ a gallon whereas ten years earlier it had sold at $1.45; baleen in the same period fell from $1.71

a pound to $1.12¾,[2] and the North Pacific fleet—those vessels operating in the Gulf of Alaska and the Okhotsk, Bering and Chukchi Seas—shrank from fifty-nine to seventeen vessels.[3] Although the annual imports of oil between 1865 and 1875 had fallen from about 76,000 to 35,000 gallons and of baleen from 619,000 to 372,000 pounds, prices had not increased because of lesser demand. In this contracting market the value of an average bowhead whale had been halved, decreasing from about $7,100 to about $3,700.[4]

These troubles struck the whaling industry after years of prosperity. In the first half of the nineteenth century, as the whaling fleets expanded their hunting territories throughout the Indian and Pacific Oceans, the continual discovery of new grounds allowed owners and merchants to pursue conservative practices in their operations: Profits and the stocks of whales remained relatively steady, so no strong stimulus for change existed. In fact, after 1750, when tryworks were first put aboard ship for rendering oil at sea, the only changes in technology or methods were minor ones.[5]

By the mid-1870's the American whaling industry had reached a crossroad. Faced with declining profits, many New England whaling merchants withdrew their ships from the fishery and invested funds in textile mills and various industrial enterprises. Others, however, accepted the challenge and turned to technological improvements as a means to increase catches. Before 1870 such innovations were largely restricted to the perfection of harpoons, darting guns, and bomb-lance shoulder guns, all relatively inexpensive inventions that merely reduced the losses of whales already struck. Yet even by this time steam power had proved itself an effective method for moving large vessels, and the British whaling and sealing fleets had employed auxiliary steamers since 1857. In 1866 a steam plant was installed in the American whaling bark *Pioneer* of New London, but the experiment did not survive the vessel's loss in the ice of Hudson Strait the following year. Nor did *Pioneer,* a converted government transport, influence the design of the class of steam whalers that began to be built twelve years later.[6]

After the Arctic disaster of 1876, the advantages of steam auxiliary power must have been in the minds of forward-

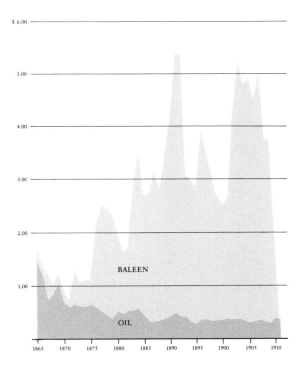

Average annual prices of whale oil (per gallon) and baleen (per pound). Sources: Reginald B. Hegarty, *Returns of Whaling Vessels Sailing from American Ports* (New Bedford, 1959), p. 51; Walter S. Tower, *A History of the American Whale Fishery* (Philadelphia, 1907), p. 128.

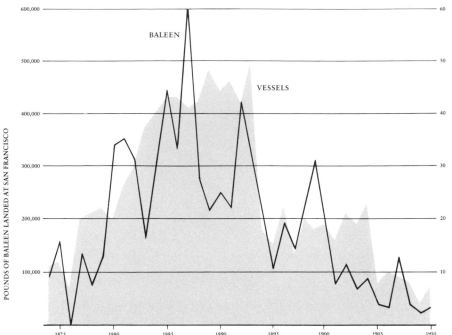

Left scale: pounds of baleen landed at San Francisco.

Right scale: number of vessels in the San Francisco whaling fleet.

Sources: Walter S. Tower, *A History of the American Whale Fishery* (Philadelphia, 1907), pp. 129-130; Annual Reports of the Chamber of Commerce of San Francisco, 1893-1906.

Frank Brown, manufacturer of darting guns and bomb-lance shoulder guns

Old Dartmouth Historical Society

Shown here in his shop in New Bedford, Frank Brown holds an early model of the bomb-lance shoulder gun, an implement used widely in the Arctic fishery. Brown joined his uncle, Ebenezer Pierce, inventor and well-known manufacturer of darting guns and shoulder guns, in 1879 and continued making whalecraft until 1923.

The bomb-lance shoulder gun was invented in 1850 by C. C. Brand and was subsequently refined in the 1870's into two basic models: one by the firm of (Ebenezer) Pierce and Eggers, the other by Cunningham and (Bernard) Cogan. In the photograph Brown holds a Brand gun. A Pierce-and-Eggers gun stands at the left. Three bombs rest on the workbench.

Exploded shoulder-gun bomb
Old Dartmouth Historical Society

Improved Temple toggle iron
Old Dartmouth Historical Society, gift of
Mr. & Mrs. F. Gilbert Hinsdale, 1959

Lewis Temple of New Bedford developed a superior whaling harpoon in 1848. Its toggling head gave it greater holding qualities than other harpoons and it soon became the standard implement in the American whaling industry.

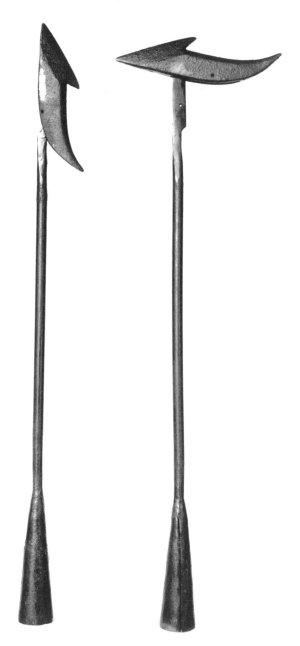

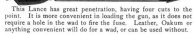
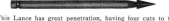

Frank Brown's whalecraft handbill
12½ x 5½ in.
Old Dartmouth Historical Society

Darting gun by Patrick Cunningham (1844-1921), stamped:
PAT APR 1882.
Old Dartmouth Historical Society, gift of
Mr. & Mrs. F. Gilbert Hinsdale, 1959.

The darting gun was developed for the Arctic fishery because
bowhead whales often escaped into the ice pack, towing lines and
gear with them. The gun, triggered by a wire rod, enabled the
whalemen to harpoon and shoot the whale in one action.

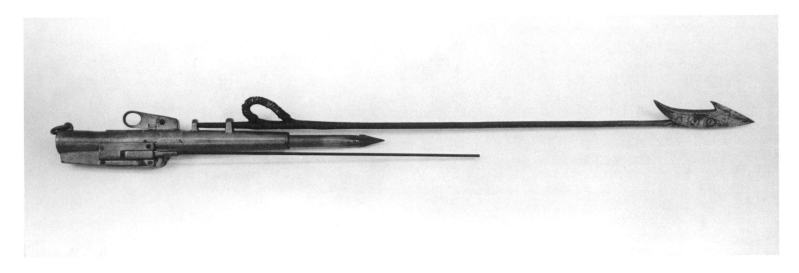

looking whaling merchants. In 1876, as in 1871, the wrecked vessels met a similar fate. Working northward along the coast of Alaska toward Point Barrow, they were caught when sudden on-shore winds forced them to anchor and left them helpless while the ice closed in upon them. A steamer, running through broken ice, against wind or current, would have been able to escape the encroaching pack.

Two other factors contributed to the development of the steam whalers: a rise in the market for baleen and the existence of the transcontinental railroad. In 1875 the demand for baleen began to increase, probably because of its growing use for corset stays and skirt hoops. The bowhead, yielding more baleen than any other whale, became the prime supplier of this market and led owners and agents of whaleships to concentrate their attentions on the Arctic grounds where it was found. After the completion of the transcontinental railroad in 1869, the products of this whale could be shipped by rail to refineries in the East faster and more cheaply than by sea around Cape Horn or across the Isthmus of Panama. As a result, the old pattern of resupplying whaleships and transshipping oil and baleen in the Hawaiian Islands was broken and in its place emerged the port of San Francisco.

The development of San Francisco altered a pattern of cruising that Yankee whalers had followed for more than thirty years. Since the 1840's whaling vessels had set out from east coast ports in early autumn for the North Pacific on voyages lasting two or more years. Rounding Cape Horn in the southern summer, or occasionally the Cape of Good Hope, they would cruise in the temperate waters of the Pacific before calling at the Hawaiian Islands in March. Refitting there for their North Pacific cruise and shipping home accumulated oil, they would sail north late in March for right whales in the Gulf of Alaska, for bowheads in the Okhotsk Sea, or—after 1848—for bowheads in Bering Strait and the Arctic Ocean. In October, at the end of the season, with ugly autumn weather chasing them, they headed once more for the Islands for fresh supplies before setting forth on a winter's cruise in the Pacific. Calling once again at Hawaii in March, they would repeat this cycle for one or two more years before returning home to New England.

Before the Civil War whaling vessels purposefully avoided San Francisco. Masters found to their dismay that the lure of the gold fields was often stronger to seamen than the prospects of several more years at sea. Large numbers of desertions occurred and the port was shunned. When the gold rush passed and as the advantages of the transcontinental railroad proved themselves, more and more whaling masters began to use the California port as a depot for resupply before and after their northern summers.

Accompanying the emergence of San Francisco as a center for the fishery were the first tentative attempts to utilize steam power to overcome the difficulties of reaching the bowheads in the ice of the Bering and Chukchi Seas. One such effort sought to use steam-powered whaleboats and launches that could be carried north aboard the whaleship, then employed to tow whaleboats to the whales and dead whales to the ship. The *Francis Palmer,* departing San Francisco in 1879, may have been the first vessel to carry a steam launch,[7] intending with it to improve its cruising range in the difficult ice east of Point Barrow. Three years later, Ivory H. Bartlett and Sons, a New Bedford firm with offices in San Francisco, provided a steam launch costing $1,250 for their bark *Rainbow* for a voyage under Captain Bernard Cogan. Both experiments were unsuccessful, apparently because the boats needed an engineer and were therefore costly to operate or often out of service.[8]

Power launches were nonetheless used in small numbers aboard whaling vessels until 1905 or later.[9] But they represented only a partial solution to the generic problem of maneuverability in the Arctic, a problem that would be more satisfactorily solved by the steam whalers until the number of bowheads decreased to such a level that even they appeared cumbersome in comparison to small gasoline-powered schooners. The comparatively insignificant cost of the steam launches—only one or two percent of the cost of a steam whaler—doubtless made them attractive to men who lacked the capital or organizational ability to build and outfit a steam whaling vessel. As usual, partial solutions are rarely successful, and sailing vessels outfitted with steam launches were never able to compete effectively with steam whalers.

The first steam whaler to operate from San Francisco was the auxiliary brig *Siberia,* a vessel built on the west coast but registered in Russia. *Siberia* made voyages to the Okhotsk Sea in 1878 and 1879 and her registry was intended to avoid possible difficulties with Russian authorities when in those waters. Although her design does not seem to have influenced the class of steam whalers, her introduction reflects the realization of her owners that more maneuverable vessels were necessary to counter declining catches in icy seas.

These developments were probably well known to William Lewis, a onetime New Bedford whaling master who turned to real-estate speculation before returning to the whaling trade as an agent for Ivory H. Bartlett and Sons. Prompted by Captain Leander Owen, an experienced Arctic whaling master and strong advocate of steam power, Lewis dispatched the veteran Captain Cyrus Manter—who in 1849 had been an officer aboard one of the first vessels to operate in the Bering Strait whaling grounds—to Newfoundland to examine the British whaling steamers from Dundee.[10] Despite what was undoubtedly a favorable report from Manter, Lewis undertook the construction of the first of the class of steam whalers, *Mary and Helen,* very much as a speculation.

Bernard Cogan
Old Dartmouth Historical Society

One of the innovative captains of the Arctic fishery, Barney Cogan experimented with a steam launch, developed a shoulder gun, and was one of the first to predict the success of wintering over at Herschel Island. His Arctic whaling career spanned almost four decades.

William Lewis
Old Dartmouth Historical Society

Leander Owen

Old Dartmouth Historical Society

Owen was one of the early proponents of steam power in the western Arctic. He served as master of the maiden voyages of William Lewis' *Mary and Helen, Belvedere,* and *North Star.*

Martin Van Buren Millard

photograph courtesy of Mystic Seaport

Master of several Arctic whaling vessels, Millard took *Mary and Helen* from New Bedford to Honolulu, then served as first mate under Leander Owen for her maiden Arctic cruise. In 1897 he saved *Belvedere* from being crushed in the ice, when two other steamers were lost, by wintering her at Peard Bay, Alaska.

To spread the costs and the risks of the venture, he enlisted not only his usual shipowning associates but also the men and firms directly involved in constructing the vessel and building her power plant. Goss, Sawyer & Packard, the Bath shipbuilders; George H. Reynolds, designer of her steam auxiliary; and C. H. Delamater, manufacturer of her power plant, all held shares of ownership.[11]

Lewis exhibited the same thorough preparedness in his selection of engineers as he had in arranging for Captain Cyrus Manter's advice. He chose George H. Reynolds to design *Mary and Helen*'s power plant because of his reputation as an engineer and for his previous experience in designing the engines for *Pioneer* of New London, the first American experiment with a steam-powered whaler, and in installing those of U.S.S. *Monitor.*[12] Reynolds' brother, Benjamin Franklin (Frank) Reynolds, formerly engineer aboard *Pioneer,* was also engaged as the engineer who would serve on *Mary and Helen.*

Mary and Helen was strongly built for coping with Arctic ice. With fine lines and bark rig, she was designed to conserve coal by using the wind on her passages to and from the Arctic and reserving her engine for times of calm or for moving among the ice floes. Only four to five tons of coal would be needed on days when the engine was in constant use. Smaller donkey engines were also provided for pumping ship, weighing anchor, and hoisting blubber.[13]

Despite the advanced features of *Mary and Helen* and the foresight invested in her by Lewis, her oil-carrying plans were essentially conservative. The hold between the main and mizzen masts was reserved for coal; forward of that she could carry 2700 barrels of oil in casks. The Dundee fleet had long been carrying blubber in iron tanks, and only a few years later the San Francisco steam whalers would adopt them, finding obvious advantages in running hot oil directly to tanks from tryworks. Otherwise, an intermediate stage of cooling was needed to prevent the wooden casks from shrinking due to the oil's heat.

Mary and Helen was launched with high expectations in Bath, Maine, on July 30, 1879. Lewis and his partners immediately brought her to New Bedford for outfitting. With her tryworks built and supplies and equipment aboard, she departed on September 9, bound for the Pacific under the command of Captain Martin Van Buren Millard. After a stormy passage through the Straits of Magellan, she reached Honolulu, where Captain Leander Owen joined her and took command for her Arctic cruise.

With an investment of $65,000 in the vessel, *Mary and Helen*'s owners anxiously awaited news of their bold experiment. When it came, it was astonishing. *Mary and Helen* arrived in San Francisco on October 10, 1880, with 2350 barrels of oil and 45,000 pounds of baleen, the product of twenty-seven bowheads and the largest catch in many years.

Mary and Helen
Charles S. Raleigh (1830-1925)
1879, oil on canvas, signed and dated lower left: "C. S. Raleigh, 1879"; 79 x 135 in.
Old Dartmouth Historical Society

With her cargo valued at more than $100,000, her investors were more than repaid after only one season's voyage. Captain Owen reported that the vessel's maneuverability in calms and adverse currents allowed him to stay in almost constant touch with the bowheads, far excelling the sailing whaleships. "We were, as whalemen say, blubber logged twice," reported Judson Cobb, one of her boatsteerers,

the first time, with twelve whales when we went and anchored off Point Franklin, boiled them out, stripped the [baleen] and stowed all below. Then we went off shore and found the whales, again filled up our blubber room and decks, and on September first we started out of the Arctic leaving plenty of whales in sight behind us, but could take no more. We came through the Behring Strait in a blinding snow storm and put into Plover Bay to finish boiling and stowing down preparatory to our start for San Francisco. Every cask we had was filled with oil; as there wasn't room enough below decks, we lashed 160 barrels on deck. As our coal was getting low, we put it all in one bunker and filled the other one with bone [baleen], and all the room between the top of the casks in the lower hold and between the decks was filled with bone too.[14]

Despite the fact that 1880 was a particularly favorable season throughout the Arctic fleet, the amazing return from *Mary and Helen* was quickly broadcast throughout the nation, and the lesson of her success was not lost on other enterprising whaling merchants.

Even before *Mary and Helen*'s return, William Lewis confidently organized another group of investors to build his second steam whaler, *Belvedere*. After *Mary and Helen*'s arrival and spurred on by her success, he proceeded to construct a third steamer, *North Star,* and arranged for the bark *Lucretia* to be converted to steam power. *North Star* was launched in August 1881 and *Lucretia* was ready for sea in the following month, both financed by the profitable sale of *Mary and Helen* to the United States Government in the spring of 1881. Lewis received $100,000 for his vessel, which was urgently needed to search for the missing *Jeannette* expedition. To replace her, he ordered the construction of *Mary and Helen* (II).

With new ships launched or ordered, Lewis's fortunes began to change. Although *Belvedere* returned from her maiden Arctic voyage with a profitable catch, the converted *Lucretia* proved to be a poor sailor. Storms prevented her from rounding Cape Horn and forced her to reach the Pacific by way of the Cape of Good Hope, too late to make the summer Arctic season. Even worse, *North Star* was crushed in the ice at Point Barrow on her maiden voyage. This loss and the failure of *Lucretia* to produce any income in 1882 compelled Lewis to sell the new *Mary and Helen* to his competitors, who took possession after she returned from her maiden Arctic voyage in 1883.

Entrepreneurs in San Francisco followed the fortunes of the first *Mary and Helen* with interest and were alive to the advantages of both steam power and San Francisco's proximity to the Arctic grounds. Early in 1881, Millen Griffith, the owner of a fleet of tugboats, George C. Perkins, a former governor of California, and Charles Goodall ordered the construction of *Bowhead,* the first of the class of steam whalers to be built on the west coast. At a cost of more than $100,000, *Bowhead* was launched on April 18, 1881. Noting the event, the San Francisco *Alta California* reported the high expectations of her owners and predicted the shift of the whaling industry from New Bedford to San Francisco.

She is without a doubt the strongest and most complete vessel ever built for the whaling business, and although our Eastern neighbors think that San Francisco will have to be satisfied with the skim milk, there is no reason why our people cannot secure the cream as well as New Bedford. Our enterprising men are determined to have it.

Like William Lewis before them, Griffith, Goodall and Perkins sensed the value of the new technology and laid the keel of a second steamer *Orca,* as soon as *Bowhead* had been launched. The group, now enlarged to include Josiah N. Knowles, then built *Narwhal* and *Balaena,* purchased *Mary and Helen* (II) from Lewis, and ordered the construction of *Thrasher* at Bath, probably because Dickie Brothers in San Francisco, the builder of their other steamers, could not handle the volume of new work. The hectic pace of activity at the yard was a source of marvel to contemporary observers. One newspaper's account of the departure of *Balaena* on April 27, 1883, relates with pride the schedule of her building:

The steam whaler *Balaena* sailed at 10 A.M. yesterday for the Arctic, completing one of the most remarkable jobs in ship building, engine construction and fitting out that has ever been performed in any port in the world. The keel of the vessel was laid on January 29th, and the builders, the Dickie Brothers, used their best endeavors to have her built in their contract time, three months, and as may be seen, they succeeded. As samples of the great and rapid jobs performed, we may mention that the engines were on the ground on Saturday, the 14th instant, yet on the following Saturday they were in position on board and the vessel was launched the same night and brought down to Vellejo Street wharf, the New Bedford of California. The rigger, Haversaith, rigged her completely and had everything in good order aloft and sails bent in one week. On the vessel reaching the wharf mentioned, although it was midnight, the work commenced, and early next morning preparations were all perfected for coaling and fitting out for sea. The stores etc. were put on board in a few hours, and coaling commenced at 5 P.M., and at 6 next morning she had her full allowance on board, 308 tons.[15]

With only the maiden voyage of *Bowhead* behind them, the partners witnessed in 1883 the maiden voyages of *Orca, Balaena* and *Narwhal,* as well as the first voyage of *Mary and Helen* (II) under their ownership—vessels valued at more

Belvedere at Petropavlovsk, Kamchatka, in 1913
photograph courtesy of Bernhard Kilian

Lucretia at Corwin Coal Mine, Alaska, in 1887
photograph courtesy of New Bedford Free Public Library

North Star's last hours
U.S. Signal Corps photograph, courtesy of the National Archives

Narwhal setting out on her maiden voyage, 1883

photograph courtesy of San Francisco Maritime Museum
(J. W. Proctor Collection)

Balaena on the stocks at the Dickie Brothers yard, San Francisco,
1883
Old Dartmouth Historical Society

Thrasher hoisting headbone aboard

Charles S. Raleigh (1830-1925)

1885, oil on canvas, signed and dated lower right: "C. S. Raleigh
1885"; 25½ x 39½

Private Collection

Josiah Nickerson Knowles, about 1890

photograph courtesy of San Francisco Maritime Museum

A native of Cape Cod, Knowles was a successful merchant skipper and later a whaling agent before he became manager of the Pacific Steam Whaling Company and its associated Arctic Oil Works.

Arctic Oil Works

Lithograph by Bosqui Engraving and Printing Company, about 1885.

photograph courtesy of The Mariners Museum

With its 300-foot wharf, the Arctic Oil Works had the advantage of allowing the Pacific Steam Whaling Company's ships (upper left) to unload directly at the refinery. Oil could be pumped into the 2000-gallon tanks or stored in casks in the flat-roofed warehouse, which had a clay floor kept damp to prevent the casks from shrinking. Refining was done in the three-story structure at the right. The one-story building in the center distance was the main baleen storage area and was fitted with double iron doors and shutters, presumably to keep out rats, and a system for flooding in case of fire.

than $500,000. But for the American fishery as a whole, the most important event of 1883 was the incorporation of the Pacific Steam Whaling Company, an event that would lead to the domination of the industry by west coast interests and bring about a surge of innovations in its practices. On October 30, 1883, Griffith, Perkins, Goodall, Knowles and others incorporated the Company "for the building, buying, selling, owning and operating of whaling and other vessels or other property, transportation of freight and passengers, trading, fishing, towing and salving; to purchase and own stocks in other corporations; to borrow and loan money; to issue bonds and conduct the business of a general whaling and trading company; to purchase, operate and own coal mines...."[16] Unlike the traditional method of owning whaleships in individual shares, investors could purchase stock in the Company itself, which was capitalized at $2,000,000.

Except for Knowles, the directors of the Company had no close contact with the whaling industry before 1880. Knowles himself, more entrepreneur than whaleman, had been a master of merchant vessels before becoming a shipping agent, then a whaling agent for William Lewis.[17] Neither he nor his partners were hindered by the traditions of the New England fishery, and perhaps as a consequence their Company successfully introduced new techniques and procedures to Arctic whaling. Flexibly organized, the Company was also able to avoid losses during slumps in the whaling industry by diverting its vessels and equipment to such endeavors as trading, salmon packing, or providing transportation to the Alaska gold fields.

Along with the incorporation of the Pacific Steam Whaling Company, the same partners established the Arctic Oil Works, the first refinery for oil and baleen on the west coast, which was capitalized at $1,000,000. Knowles was appointed manager of both the Oil Works and the Company, and under his direction the two enterprises provided for all the basic processes from catching to refining in what was essentially one organization. In establishing the Oil Works, the partners assumed that oil from their Arctic fleet could be refined more cheaply and sold more profitably on the Pacific coast than if it were shipped to the East for processing. F. A. Booth, a New Bedford man experienced in the procedures of the east coast refineries, was engaged as superintendent and the plant was erected on the Company's wharf in the Potrero district of San Francisco. The location had the obvious advantage of allowing the Company's vessels to be berthed directly at the site of the refinery.[18]

The Company's ships, like William Lewis', were well built[19] with fine, clean lines for fast passages to and from the Arctic grounds. But unlike Lewis' vessels, the Company's *Bowhead* and *Orca* were fitted with large two-bladed propellers from which the shafts could be withdrawn, allowing them to be hoisted in a sliding frame up into the vessel.[20] A

Drying baleen in the Arctic Oil Works yard
Old Dartmouth Historical Society
After arrival in San Francisco, baleen was dried to prevent mildew. In the distance are *Orca* (left) and the bark *J. D. Peters* (right), a company freighter.

Balaena and *Orca* berthed at the Arctic Oil Works wharf
photograph courtesy of San Francisco Maritime Museum

Orca's propeller well

Detail of a model lent by the Museum of History and Technology, Smithsonian Institution

Old Dartmouth Historical Society

centerboard was then placed in the void to improve speed under sail. *Orca, Thrasher, Narwhal,* and *Balaena,* were also equipped with steam tryworks and iron oil tanks.[21] The tryworks or "steam digesters" not only speeded the process of rendering oil from blubber, but left the oil with a lighter color and less odor than that from blubber-fired tryworks. The oil could then be transferred directly to the iron holding tanks without first cooling it, as was necessary when using wooden casks. The tanks also allowed the ship's load to be trimmed while at sea by pumping oil from one tank to another.[22] With these new methods of rendering and storing oil, the vessels of the Pacific Steam Whaling Company anticipated some types of equipment that characterize the factory ships of twentieth-century whaling.

Josiah N. Knowles, in all likelihood the motivating force behind many of the Pacific Steam Whaling Company's innovations, regarded efficiency and cost-cutting as important, but also tried to improve catches. One bold move that he took in this direction, with far-reaching implications for the history of northern Alaska, was the establishment of shore-based whaling and trading stations on that coast. For although the steam whalers were reaping good returns, many masters realized that great numbers of whales were making their passage into the Beaufort Sea while the ice was still too heavy to allow pursuit. Knowles was therefore receptive to a suggestion made in the autumn of 1883 that a station be established at Point Barrow from which whales could be hunted by the Eskimo method of catching them at the narrow ice leads in the springtime. The plan was proposed by Edward Perry (Ned) Herendeen, an experienced Arctic whaler recently returned from a two-year tour at Point Barrow as interpreter for a U.S. Army Signal Corps expedition. Knowles was probably familiar already with shore whaling on the coast of California for gray whales, and the practice, if adopted in the Arctic, held further potential for trading for baleen with the natives. In 1884 he decided to act on the proposal and sent out a group to winter at Point Barrow. They were not successful the first year, but as a result of the 1886 season, Knowles was encouraged to expand his operations to Point Hope in 1887. The two stations eventually proved profitable, and, like many of the Pacific Steam Whaling Company's innovations, were widely copied by others.

Contrary to the predictions of whalemen who believed the steamers too noisy and frightening to whales,[23] these vessels consistently proved their value by tracking the increasingly elusive bowheads into difficult or dangerous locations. Usually leaving San Francisco in March—or in December if they first intended to visit the Japan grounds—most of the steamers arrived in April at Dutch Harbor on Unalaska Island in the Aleutians. Coal and supplies would be taken on and codfish caught for salting before they headed north toward Ber-

Whaling masters meeting at Port Clarence
photograph courtesy of New Bedford Free Public Library

Steam whaler at anchor in Port Clarence, 1899
Old Dartmouth Historical Society (R. Swain Gifford Collection)

Eskimos aboard *Alexander* for trading at Port Clarence
photograph courtesy of Dukes County Historical Society

Thrasher iced up after an autumn gale in the Arctic Ocean, 1887
photograph courtesy of New Bedford Free Public Library

Towing casks ashore for water, Port Clarence
photograph courtesy of San Francisco Maritime Museum

ing Strait. Some of the others would enter the Bering Sea by way of the "Seventy-two" or Amukta Pass through the Aleutians, but thereafter all would face the problem of working through the ice after the bowheads. The ice would be met in mid-April, roughly on a line from Cape Navarin to St. Matthew and Nunivak Islands, and would force the steamers to work their way towards Bering Strait through leads in the pack. Once in the pack, they could be crushed if wind or current drove the ice upon them, but their masters were judged by their catches and knew that chances had to be taken if whales were to be caught. From experience they knew that the leads in the pack often opened in two areas: an eastern route that began near St. Matthew Island and allowed them to work northwards toward St. Lawrence Island, and a western route, beginning at Cape Navarin and along shore into Anadyr Gulf. Once in the Gulf, the vessels would coast along the south shore of the Chukotsk Peninsula to Plover (Provideniya) Bay, Indian Point (Cape Chaplin) and then to St. Lawrence Island, watching for whales along the way and trading with natives for baleen, furs, walrus ivory, and Arctic clothing and footwear. As the ice allowed, they would then work north into Bering Strait, whaling and trading as they went.[24]

Rarely were the steamers able to force their way through the melting floes into the Arctic Ocean until late June, and by that time most of the bowheads had rounded Point Barrow into the Beaufort Sea. Much of the fleet would therefore head for Port Clarence, a spacious, secure harbor, to take on water, carry out repairs, and meet their resupply tenders for mail, fresh provisions, and coal. "Spring catches" of baleen and oil would be transferred to the tenders, thereby preventing a total loss for a voyage should a ship be lost later in the season.

It was in the "fall season" that the steamers proved most productive. Leaving Port Clarence after celebrating the Fourth of July, all vessels, whether sail or steam, would work their way north through Bering Strait, reaching Point Hope about July 10. Some steamers would then go to Corwin Coal Mine, operated by the Pacific Steam Whaling Company, to top up their bunkers. By late July the fleet would pass Icy Cape and begin to work its way along the Alaska coast to the dangerous waters off Point Barrow. Once safely past the treacherous Blossom Shoals, the whalers tread softly, for the movement of ice was far less predictable than further south and the pack, even in summer, was never far from shore. Sudden changes in the wind could bring it swiftly down upon the coast, crushing even the strongest craft. The sailing vessels, often hampered by light airs or adverse winds and currents, proceeded with extreme caution in the waters beyond Icy Cape; the steamers, granted favorable ice conditions, could travel quickly and boldly to Point Barrow, or even east of there, to await the bowheads as they returned from their summer feeding grounds in the eastern Beaufort Sea. After whaling near Point Barrow for three to four weeks, they would leave the area and its encroaching ice at the beginning of September to follow the whales to their autumn feeding grounds near Herald Island.

In the deepening autumn twilight the steamers would join the sailing vessels on these productive grounds. But the sailers were never able to stay late into the season, being dependent on wind to make their passage out. As the days passed, they became especially vulnerable, threatened by cold of late September and early October, which could freeze the sea to as much as six inches during a calm night.[25] In 1879, the New Bedford barks *Mount Wollaston* and *Vigilant* were trapped and lost by such a freeze,[26] while the bark *Helen Mar* escaped only by setting all sails in a gale and forcing herself through the thickening slush for forty-eight hours, making less than a knot. After reaching open water, her crew found all of her ice sheathing cut through by abrasion and all but an eighth of an inch of her planking worn away.[27] Steamers, of course, with their power, their iron shoeing on the stem, and their greenheart sheathing could cut through more than five inches of young ice,[28] but even so, most of them made it a rule of thumb to pass through Bering Strait by the tenth of October. Sailing vessels found it prudent to leave by late September, thus relinquishing the late autumn season which often proved the most productive.

Throughout the 1880's the steamers continued to return profitable catches, and the fleet grew as the price of baleen rose. The Pacific Steam Whaling Company added the steamers *Grampus* in 1886 and *Jesse H. Freeman* two years later, and in 1888. William Lewis built the steamer that bore his name. The masters of these vessels, growing confident in the capabilities of steam, pushed farther and farther east of Point Barrow, following the whales. In 1882 they passed the Colville River Delta[29] and in 1888 Captain George F. Bauldry in *Orca* reached Barter Island, the most easterly point yet attained by a whaler from Bering Strait.[30] Since the 1850's, whalemen knew that British explorers had seen large numbers of bowheads in what was later to be named Amundsen Gulf,[31] more than 700 nautical miles east of Point Barrow, but were wary of the possibility of being frozen in or crushed by ice so far from hope of rescue. In 1874 Charles M. Scammon wrote in his *Marine Mammals of the North-western Coast of North America* of the potentials of the area, pointing out that the "remote line of open water, inaccessible to ships, between the summer ice border and the northern shores of the American continent, from Point Barrow to Banks' Land, doubtless affords ample herding and breeding places for the [bowheads]."[32]

By the late 1870's, the theory that the summer grounds of the bowheads were located in the waters near the Mackenzie River Delta and Cape Bathurst, was generally accepted.[33] Thus, when the bark *Francis Palmer* left San Francisco in 1879 carrying a steam launch, it was hoped a crew could use it to reach the Mackenzie Delta.[34] Although unsuccessful, the experiment illustrates the strong current of interest that existed to investigate the speculations of Scammon and others.

Whalemen were understandably cautious about venturing along the coast north and east of Icy Cape. No good harbors were known and there the ice pack acted as a hammer on the anvil of the shore. After the establishment of the Pacific Steam Whaling Company's shore station at Point Barrow, the shore-based whalemen found themselves in greater contact with the natives, and in 1887 a returning Eskimo trader confirmed suspicions that bowheads were numerous in the shallow waters off the Mackenzie Delta. As a result, the resi-dent manager of the station, Charles Brower, outfitted one of his harpooneers, Joe Tuckfield, with a whaleboat and sent him east with several Eskimos to spend the winter of 1888-1889 and investigate the reports.[35]

The significance of Tuckfield's departure was understood by many, for on November 16, 1888, long before his return, the San Francisco *Chronicle* reported:

For some time past the whalemen have been told by natives that quantities of whalebone could be procured at Herschel Island, but as they never reached that point the story is doubted. This year, however, a venturesome boatsteerer has gone with a party of natives in a whaleboat to visit the island and as far eastward as he can get. The result of the journey will be known to the whalemen in August next, when they arrive at Point Barrow, and it is safe to state that if whales or whalebone are to be had at Herschel Island that a vessel will endeavor to reach that point.

Tuckfield wintered in the Mackenzie Delta and returned in early August 1889, reporting that whales were indeed plentiful, that he had caught one, and—most important of all—that Herschel Island possessed a good harbor.[36] Although the significance of his thousand-mile, open-boat voyage has been overlooked, he deserves consideration as the herald of the opening of the Herschel Island fishery. On August 2, on his return voyage, he met a fleet of seven steamers[37] near the Colville Delta and reported his news. Having taken few whales that season, the whalers were anxious to make a catch and pushed on to the east, reaching Herschel Island on August 11 and the Delta shortly afterwards. A few days later *Beluga* and U.S.S. *Thetis* joined the ships at Herschel, the latter having been sent to establish the position of the 141st meridian west of Greenwich, the boundary between the United States and Canada on the Arctic coast. At Herschel her crew briefly surveyed the island and sounded the harbor, naming it Pauline Cove.[38]

Before returning to Point Barrow at the end of the summer, the whalers briefly assessed the potentials of this whaling ground. Finding indications of the presence of whales, even though few were taken, they noted the relatively ice-free seas compared to the conditions at Point Barrow, as well as

Pauline Cove from the east, 1970

photograph courtesy of Paul Fenimore Cooper, Jr.

The large building on the sandspit is the whalers' community store house, built in 1893.

The first chart of Herschel Island, made from the survey by U.S.S. *Thetis*

Private collection

This chart, published in March 1890, was used on board *Mary D. Hume* on her first wintering voyage.

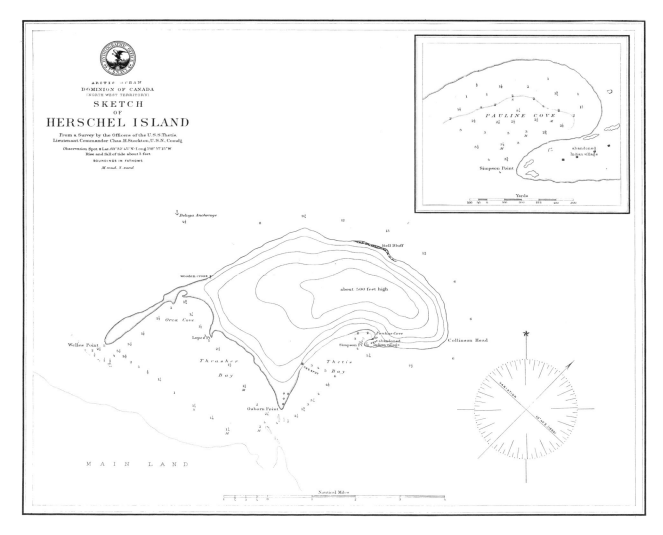

George F. Bauldry

photograph courtesy of The Mariners Museum (Albert M. Barnes Collection)

A runaway farm boy from England, Bauldry first sailed on whalers out of New London, Connecticut. He rose to the rank of captain in 1869 and was one of the first officers to understand the importance of the darting gun for the Arctic fishery. In the 1880's, Bauldry sailed for the Pacific Steam Whaling Company, commanding *Balaena*, *Thrasher*, and *Orca*.

the good harbor, the presence of game on land, and the possibility of escaping up the Mackenzie River, should they be trapped by the ice.[39] Impressions such as these doubtless stimulated plans for wintering at Herschel. Gilbert B. Borden, keeper of the federal government's refuge station at Point Barrow, wrote to Frederick Swift, a whaling merchant in New Bedford, as soon as the news reached him. Tuckfield, he reported, "returned with accounts that made almost everybody crazy, of the great amount of whales down there. . . . The way Joe expresses it is 'that whales are thick as bees.' The beaches are lined with driftwood so there be no danger of freezing and there is plenty of game, with ammunition there be no danger of starving."[40]

The idea of wintering over in the Arctic was hardly novel. Vessels of the Royal Navy had carried out many highly-publicized winterings in the Arctic during the 1850's while searching for the missing expedition of Sir John Franklin, and as early as 1849, Lieutenant Matthew Fontaine Maury, Superintendent of the U.S. Naval Observatory, had suggested the possibility of whalers wintering in the Arctic to take bowheads, prophetically calling for the use of steam vessels.[41] American whaling vessels had, in fact, successfully wintered in Hudson Bay since 1861, and only the lack of knowledge about good harbors may have inhibited the practice in the western Arctic. One experienced and venturesome whaleman, George F. Bauldry, proposed a western Arctic wintering after returning in 1885 with a poor catch.[42] On such a voyage, he said, it would be possible to meet the whales as they arrived on their feeding grounds in early summer without the difficulty of fighting through the ice at Point Barrow.

The first attempt to winter over began early in 1889, before the harbor at Herschel Island had been discovered. Captain Louis N. Herendeen—the brother of Ned Herendeen, who originated the Arctic shore whaling concept—believed that a light vessel with shallow draft could find winter quarters near the Mackenzie Delta or at Cape Bathurst. He obtained the backing of a San Francisco whaling firm for a twenty-seven-month voyage aboard the little 69-ton coasting schooner *Nicoline*.[43] The voyage was a failure, for although well conceived, it was thwarted by misfortune. After a slow passage north, the schooner arrived at Point Barrow too late to reach Herschel and was forced to winter in Dease Inlet.[44] The following spring the crew engaged in shore whaling at Point Barrow but took no whales. On reaching Herschel in the autumn of 1890, *Nicoline* was joined by two Pacific Steam Whaling Company vessels, but because of a shortage of supplies she was forced to leave early the following summer without having taken a whale on her two-year voyage.

The first successful plans for wintering were formed nearly six months after Herendeen embarked on *Nicoline*. After the return of the steamers from their first visit to Herschel in the

James A. Tilton, about 1910
Old Dartmouth Historical Society

autumn of 1889, Albert Norwood and James Tilton, both experienced Arctic whalemen and first mates on Pacific Steam Whaling Company ships, heard of Herendeen's venture. Realizing its potential value, they approached Josiah Knowles for the backing of the Company for wintering voyages.[45] Knowles, Norwood, and Tilton no doubt agreed that a steamer, rather than a sailing vessel, should be used because of its greater mobility in the ice conditions they were likely to encounter. Knowles found the proposal acceptable, and with characteristically sound planning, he set about organizing the operation. He assigned Norwood the steamer *Grampus*—the former U.S. revenue cutter *Richard Rush,* which the Company had bought from the government in 1886 and re-rigged for whaling—and he bought the little 90-foot steam schooner *Mary D. Hume* for Tilton.[46]

As the smallest vessels in the Company's steam fleet, *Grampus* and *Mary D. Hume* were considered best suited for cruising in the shallow waters near the Mackenzie Delta.[47] Although *Grampus* was probably fitted with tryworks when rigged for whaling in 1886, *Mary D. Hume* did not carry them. Their absence was of little consequence to Knowles, who watched the skyrocketing price of baleen and ordered his captains to "take no oil, nothing but whalebone."[48] It would be far more profitable to cut out the baleen as quickly as possible and return for more, rather than pause to "spade out fat."[49]

Mary D. Hume and *Grampus* left San Francisco in the spring of 1890. Early in July, they met the fleet's tender at Port Clarence, then pushed on to Point Barrow to take on a final load of supplies.[50] Heading east on August 2, they passed the *Nicoline,* also bound for Herschel, and arrived at the island eighteen days later. The crews commenced unloading supplies, then built a warehouse on the sandspit at Pauline Cove. By September 15, the three vessels were frozen in and the men began preparations for the long winter. In doing this, they established procedures that other ships would follow for more than twenty years. Before the ice had locked the vessels in, each crew collected at least a hundred cords of driftwood, stacking it on the sandspit, where it was daily sawed and split for firewood.[51] Extra stores and the ships' boats were also put on shore in case fire should break out aboard a vessel. Sod was cut from the thick tundra turf to insulate the tops of the vessels' houses and decks were roofed over with lumber and canvas. As snow accumulated, blocks were cut out of the wind-compacted ridges and used to bank the ship in, insulating against the penetrating cold. Ice from a fresh-water pond was sawn into blocks, which were stored on racks on the sandspit to provide drinking water throughout the winter. As the harbor ice thickened, men were assigned to the duty of chopping it free from the rudder and propeller in order to protect these vulnerable parts from damage.

A boat from *Belvedere* collecting driftwood near Herschel Island, 1912
photograph courtesy of the American Museum of Natural History

First winter at Herschel Island
photograph courtesy of Dukes County Historical Society
Grampus (left) and *Mary D. Hume* (right) are banked with snow for insulation. The *Hume*'s deck has been roofed over.

Belvedere banked with snow and roofed over at Herschel Island, 1906-1907
photograph courtesy of the Stefansson Collection, Dartmouth College

Hartson Bodfish at Point Barrow, 1892
photograph courtesy of the Presbyterian Historical Society

During the winter supplies of fresh meat were obtained through trade with sixty Eskimos, who camped near the ship in their snow houses, and with Indians, who crossed the mountains south of Herschel to make occasional visits. The meat, which was valuable for preventing scurvy and consisted of caribou, ptarmigan, and goose, was stored in underground cellars which were made by blasting craters in the permanently frozen ground, then roofed over with logs and sod. The ships' younger officers also contributed to the meat supply by making long hunting trips into the interior. Hartson H. Bodfish, first mate of *Mary D. Hume,* was one of the first to undertake what became a regular Herschel practice. Living with an Eskimo family at their island camp and wearing Eskimo dress, Bodfish spent most of the winter hunting and returned to Herschel only for provisions.[52]

By comparison with later experiences, the winter of 1890-1891 passed fairly well for the men at Herschel. No cases of scurvy were reported and Bodfish noted that his only serious complaint was the loss of skin from his tongue when it froze to the metal horn he blew to celebrate New Year's Eve at −30°F. Lack of knowledge about the means of protection from extreme cold caused the most problems, particularly cases of frostbite. As usual aboard whaling vessels, captains and officers were called upon in time of need to perform surgical operations, and often carried them out with skill.[53] That winter Bodfish began the long series of emergency operations that would continue for nearly twenty years. His initiation as a field surgeon was at his own expense, for on the voyage to Herschel his toe was crushed by a falling topmast block.

When I had taken a survey of the damage I knew that I must lose a toe. So I sent the steward for the captain to do the job, but he was busy at the time and asked me to wait.

I thought rather fast. My foot was numb from the accident. I knew that the longer I waited, the more painful the amputation would be, so, with the steward and cabin boy looking on and groaning, I whetted up my knife and cut it off myself. The way it was injured made it necessary for me to unjoint the bone from the foot, too, but I did it, and there was considerable satisfaction in having performed my first surgical operation.[54]

Discussing the problem of frozen toes, he wrote to his mother with delight about his newfound skill:

I tell you Capt. Tilton and I missed our vocation when we started whaling. We ought to have been surgeons. We administer chloroform and off with them. So far everything has turned out all right and none of our patients have died on us. I think there will be a "corner" on toes when all get back to Frisco, as three of us lost eight, and I think two more will have to go. If father hadn't bought a livery stable I think I would have been a doctor.[55]

Among the foremast hands the problems of restlessness and boredom from inactivity, which were to break out violently in following years, resulted in the desertions of six men.[56] With the sun below the horizon from the twenty-ninth of November to the twelfth of January, the temperature dropping to forty below zero, and the nearest settlement four hundred miles away, there was little chance for the men who tried to run away. "At first it was not the intention to go after them," Bodfish wrote, "but it was found that they had stolen so much that a search for them was made. They were found at a native's house about seven hours travel from the ship by dog team. They were all frozen very badly. . . . They had slept out of doors one night when the thermometer was thirty below zero, they were very glad to be caught."[57]

As the summer of 1891 approached, the men of the *Mary D. Hume*, still seeking their first whale, were anxious to begin the hunt for bowheads. In an attempt at shore whaling, they dragged their boats over fifteen miles of ice to an open lead off the north end of the island. The second mate, George B. Leavitt, went a step further and cruised in a whaleboat for two weeks through the broken ice of late spring. Neither venture was successful, but the officers and crew of the *Hume* were still determined to take whales. Although *Nicoline*, short of provisions, would be forced to leave for home as soon as the ice allowed and *Grampus* intended to depart in August, the men on the *Hume* decided to stick to their original plan and stay for another winter. Such a schedule not only would permit the greatest possible cruising time, but would enable them to go, as Bodfish wrote, "to that great undiscovered country that lies to the eastward of us," where he hoped that it would "turn out to be the great 'El Dorado' that we expect."[58]

The ships left Pauline Cove about July 10, 1891. *Mary D. Hume* headed eastward and reached Cape Bathurst by July 27. Four days later, she found her "El Dorado," and from that time until September 24, her men caught twenty-seven whales. A brief return to Herschel was required "to land bone, the ship being burdened too greatly with it too allow [the men] to work freely."[59] *Grampus* was at the Island, nearly as successful with twenty-one whales, and took on some of the *Hume*'s baleen when she departed for San Francisco in August.

The second winter at Herschel, without other crews to share the monotony, was harder on the *Hume*'s men. Boredom and loneliness descended heavily and scurvy broke out. The first of many winter deaths to occur during the island's whaling phase occurred when John Meyers, a sixty-year-old black seaman from Baltimore, died of "inflammatory rheumatism" on March 17, 1892. His body was buried in the snow and covered with logs until the ground thawed enough to allow a proper burial on the shore of Pauline Cove.

Having received no news since 1890, the men were anxious for word from the outside world. William Mogg, the third mate, walked three hundred miles southward, crossing over the mountains and below the tree line, to Rampart House, a Hudson's Bay Company outpost and Anglican missionary station. When he arrived, the missionaries, also starved for news, were able only to tell him that Queen Victoria was alive and that Lord Salisbury was still prime minister. When so informed, Bodfish wrote that this was "wonderful news for a bunch of New England Yankees who had received no mail for over twenty-six months!"[60] And Mogg was reported as saying as he left the missionaries at Rampart House that "he needed their prayers to protect him from damnation for profanity on the return tramp."[61]

The *Hume* made her way out of the ice at Herschel on July 4, 1892, and reached Cape Bathurst on July 28. The crew again took whales rapidly until starting for home on August 15. When their vessel arrived in San Francisco on September 30, after twenty-nine months absence, the news was electrifying: she had taken the baleen of thirty-seven whales and her cargo was valued at $400,000. Her voyage was clearly among the most profitable in all of American whaling history.[62] A newspaper reporter provided further details for San Francisco readers:

The little steamer *Mary D. Hume*, which made the phenomenal take of whales at the mouth of the McKenzie River . . . arrived in the bay at an early hour yesterday morning. The boarding house masters swarmed out to her until the Hume's progress was almost checked by a wall of whitehall boats two to three deep all around her. . . . Several of her crew are suffering from contracted muscles, due to scurvy and rheumatism, contracted during the first season. The Hume had not reached the oil works wharf, however, before nearly every man had left her

The sailors looked like a lot of wild men when they came ashore; they had long hair, longer beards and clothing that was patched and tattered beyond recognition of the original hue and texture of the garments. There were only three pairs of shoes in the party, the remainder of the crew being shod with deerskin and rubbers.[63]

Even before the triumphant return of *Mary D. Hume*, the news from Herschel had reached San Francisco. *Grampus*'s arrival in the autumn of 1891 had already stimulated the Pacific Steam Whaling Company to outfit *Narwhal*, *Balaena*, *Newport*, and *Grampus* herself for wintering voyages. To support these vessels and enable them to take full advantage of the short summer season, the Company arranged for a supply ship, the 862-ton, four-masted steam schooner *Jeanie*, to sail for Herschel. Aboard her would be fresh supplies and men to relieve those who had served their stint, while on her return *Jeanie* would bring out the accumulated baleen. By this move, the Company established what was in fact an advance Arctic base that would permit *Newport* and *Mary D. Hume* to remain in the north continuously for six years. Indeed, these two vessels, both lacking tryworks, anticipated the modern concept of the shore-based catcher ship that brings its baleen and blubber to a land station for processing and shipment.

Newport cutting in
John Bertonccini (1872-1947)
Ca. 1896, oil on canvas, 15½ x 26 in.
Private collection

Not until the *Hume*'s return did other whaling merchants venture to outfit ships for wintering voyages. In 1892, a San Francisco meat-packing concern, Roth, Blum and Company, built the steam brigantine *Jeanette*[64] and introduced the former salmon steamer *Karluk* to the fishery. As word came in of the successful seasons of 1893 and 1894 and the record catches of sixty-four whales by *Narwhal* and sixty-two by *Balaena,* more entered the Herschel Island fishery. Captain James McKenna, master of the steamer *Alliance* in 1885 and 1886, bought *Fearless* in Norway and sailed her to the Arctic for the 1894 season. In the same year, Wright, Bowne and Company sent out the old steam bark *Alexander,* and William Lewis dispatched his newly-converted *William Baylies* and *Navarch* to Herschel. Several sailing vessels were also fitted for wintering voyages.

From 1893 to 1895, a fleet of ships steamed or sailed past Point Barrow to the "20-25 fathom ground," where *Mary D. Hume* had struck it rich. Stretching from the Mackenzie Delta to Cape Bathurst, these waters were far enough from the river's nutrient-rich outflow that its silt had settled, allowing sunlight to penetrate and trigger the rich plankton blooms that fed the whales. Here, in this last refuge of the bowheads, the whalers of the 1890's made their greatest catches, harvests made possible by the winter base at Herschel.

During the winter of 1894-1895, fifteen vessels wintered at Herschel. In the following year, thirteen did so, and the settlement by that time confronted all the problems found in any Arctic boom town. With as many as five hundred whalemen wintering there, the first problem was to insure an adequate supply of fresh food to combat scurvy. Preferring caribou to fish, both of which were plentiful, the whalers obtained it through trade with Eskimos and Indians who soon began to visit the settlement because of the higher prices for meat and furs paid by the whalers than by the Hudson's Bay Company trading posts in the interior. In this enterprise the "Itkilliks," the whalemen's term for the Indians of the Mackenzie River drainage, were more frequent visitors than the "Kogmollits," the Delta Eskimos, who seemed content to subsist on fish. Most productive of all the native groups, however, were the "Nunatarmas," or Eskimos of the north Alaskan interior who moved east to take advantage of the trade at Herschel. Primarily caribou hunters, aggressive and ambitious,[65] they supplied the bulk of the trade meat at Herschel.

The whalers also brought native families to Herschel, both Chukchees and Eskimos, which they signed on as they made their way north, stopping to trade at St. Lawrence Island, Plover Bay, Indian Point, East Cape, the Diomede Islands, Point Hope or Point Barrow. Hired as boatsteerers, deckhands, seamstresses, contract hunters, or dog drivers, these natives would set up hunting camps in the mountains

Jeanette in the ice at Point Barrow, August 1898
Private collection

Karluk in 1913
photograph courtesy of the Public Archives of Canada

south of Herschel, sometimes as much as two hundred miles away[66] and send in whatever game was available. The consumption of caribou, mountain sheep, moose, fish and ptarmigan[67] at Herschel was at times prodigious. Andrew Jackson Stone, a naturalist who traveled to the island in 1896, estimated that each ship at Herschel accounted for more than 10,000 pounds of caribou meat a year.[68]

With so many people living in close quarters, problems inevitably cropped up. Enforced idleness and rumors of gold on the upper Yukon River combined to cause desertions every winter. Few deserters made good their escape; many froze to death and many returned badly frostbitten. Occasionally groups of men left their ships together, as did seventeen on January 21, 1896, and twelve more on March 12. A party of officers and Eskimos was sent after them because "as long as any number of deserters remained at large, it was a temptation to other men to desert and join them."[69] With the second group, running gun battles occurred more than a hundred miles from Herschel, resulting in the deaths of two of the deserters.[70]

Alcohol caused its familiar troubles. Although the Pacific Steam Whaling Company prohibited its employees from selling or trading whiskey[71] and despite the fact that most captains were opposed to the trade,[72] a traffic in alcohol existed, and gun-barrel stills were erected on shore in native huts by both whalemen and Eskimos. The stills were periodically broken up, first by ships' officers, later by policemen and missionaries, but whiskey was never entirely suppressed. The alcohol, combined with the isolation and idleness, created problems identical to those found today in northern towns from Frobisher to Nome. Drunkeness, rape, abductions, assaults, murder and suicide all occurred from time to time at Herschel.

Debauchery at Herschel has been highlighted by writers —romantic, xenophobic, or misinformed—with descriptions of a "baccanalian orgy which beggared description." Down the gangplanks, according to one excited author, "surged a motley horde of mixed humanity till the sandpit was overrun with a drunken mob of dark-visaged kanakas, bearded Russians, ebony-faced Negroes, and the off-scouring of the Barbary Coast. Rum flowed like water. Fighting, drinking, and debauchery became the order of the day."[73] Had Herschel been like this, few whaling masters would have wintered there or have brought their wives along. According to police inspector D. M. Howard the wild reports appearing in newspapers were greatly exaggerated: "the Esquimaux greeting at the ships' arrival belies stories of abuse and mistreatment; the women would certainly stay away."[74]

Because of the growing numbers of Eskimos at Herschel, the Anglican missionary at Fort Macpherson, Isaac O. Stringer, visited the island in November 1893[75] on the first of many trips that he and his successor, C. E. Whittaker,

Siberian Eskimo at Herschel Island, 1895
photograph courtesy of The Mariners Museum

Graves at Herschel Island, 1917
photograph courtesy of the California Academy of Sciences

Herschel Island in 1893-1894

John Bertonccini (1872-1947)

Ca. 1894, oil on canvas, signed lower left: "J. Bertonchini";
19 x 32 in.

*Old Dartmouth Historical Society, gift of Mr. and Mrs.
Eliot D. Stetson, Jr., 1971*

This bird's-eye view of Pauline Cove depicts (left to right) the
brigantine *Mary D. Hume*, barkentine *Newport*, bark *Grampus*,
brigantine *Jeanette*, bark *Narwhal*, brigantine *Karluk*, and bark
Balaena. On shore are five whalers' store houses surrounding the
larger community store house, several Eskimo houses, fresh-water
ice on stages, two coal piles, and the ships' whaleboats under
snow banks. The men amuse themselves with soccer, baseball,
and skiing.

Bishop Stringer (left) and Archdeacon Whittaker (right) at
Herschel Island, 1917
photograph courtesy of the California Academy of Sciences

Sergeant Fitzgerald (right) at Herschel Island, about 1905
photograph courtesy of Mariners Museum

John Bertonccini, about 1900

photograph courtesy of San Francisco Maritime Museum

John Bertonccini, known as "Johnny the Painter," was one of the
few whalemen-artists from the steam-whaling era in the western
Arctic. Born in Stockholm, Sweden, in 1872, the son of an Italian
immigrant who painted theater scenery, he appears to have made
his first voyage to the Arctic on *Newport* in 1892. From then until
the 1930's he was in the Arctic nearly continuously on whalers
and trading vessels.

would make.[76] Eventually Stringer took up permanent residence and established an Anglican mission at Herschel in 1897.[77] He enjoyed good relations with the whaling masters, but reported in 1897 that there was still "a great deal of evil to contend with," although there was less drunkenness than in former years.[78]

The Canadian government understandably viewed with growing concern this large foreign incursion into its territory. Missionary reports of abuses and the complaint of the Hudson's Bay Company over the whalemen's intrusion on its trade monopoly with the Eskimos[79] spurred the government to emphasize its sovereignty by establishing a Northwest Mounted Police post at the island. In November 1903, Sergeant Fitzgerald and Corporal Munro arrived for the winter,[80] apparently welcomed by the masters of whaleships, whose authority over their crews would be reinforced by the presence of the police.

Life at Herschel was not all disorderly. Sports, games and a social life of sorts provided diversions during the long winter. In the summer of 1893, when seven ships arrived at Pauline Cove, men from all the crews constructed a communal store house that contained a game and billard room. The house still stands and may be the oldest frame structure in the Yukon Territory, being built well before the Klondike gold rush. Minstrel shows and theatricals were performed in it, and it served generally as a focal point for indoor activities throughout the winter. The men also amused themselves by skiing and tobogganing on the hills on the north side of the cove and by playing baseball and soccer on the harbor ice. A baseball league was organized with four teams contending: the Herschels, Northern Lights, Arctics, and Pick-ups.

The winter of 1894-1895 was the first in which the wives of whaling masters came to Herschel. Five of them, several with children, added a certain flair to the social life of the island. Masters with wives soon became known as "the Four Hundred"; those without them organized into "Hoodlums" and "Dry Throats." Elaborate parties were given among the three groups, and although the women were in short supply, one captain wrote that he had a fine time at one affair, where "for a partner in the Virginia Reel I had Miss Dorothy Porter aged 5 years."[81] The last event of the season, the Fourth of July, was celebrated as the ships prepared for their release from Herschel's ice with salutes, flying flags, and obstacle races.

Even as the pattern of wintering life became routine, events were bringing changes. Catches of baleen fell steadily from 1892 to 1895 and remained low in 1896 and 1897. The Pacific Steam Whaling Company, well aware that it could not rely on rising prices to offset declining catches, began to explore ways to increase productivity and cut costs. One attempt, which was unsuccessful from the start, sought to

A fancy dress party at Herschel Island, probably 1895-1896
Private collection

Back row (left to right): Mrs. George Porter, George B. Leavitt, James A. Wing, Hartson Bodfish, James McKenna. Front row: Mrs. F. M. Green, Lucy (?) Cook, Mrs. John Cook, unidentified, Mrs. Joseph Whiteside, Dorothy Porter.

Herschel Island social invitations
Private collection

Fourth-of-July celebration at Herschel, 1896

Old Dartmouth Historical Society

An obstacle race is in progress and the best seats seem to be on the roof of the community store house.

Herschel Island, 1906

photograph courtesy of Stefansson Collection, Dartmouth College

reduce the master's share of the proceeds of a voyage. His income, on a share of the net proceeds, rather than a salary, could run as high as $10,000 or more. From the Company's viewpoint, the fact that Arctic whaling masters usually did not "lower" a boat or participate in the actual killing of whales, made that share seem exorbitant. As whales in the eastern Beaufort Sea were found in concentrations in only a few, well-known areas, any competent navigator, whether a whaleman or merchant skipper, should be able to take the vessel to them—or so the Company reasoned as it set about hiring merchant masters at a salary of $175 a month. The scheme was flawed, as Captain Bodfish pointed out, because the salaried skipper was unlikely to have the knowledge or incentive to command a vessel with the skill of those who had worked their way up in the fishery. Arctic whaling was simply too specialized an enterprise to risk its direction in the hands of mariners, however competent, who were unfamiliar with the whaling trade.[82]

To increase catches, extra boats were added to some vessels.[83] Another initiative, not judged successful, was to winter farther east than Herschel in order to have earlier access to the bowheads' summer feeding grounds. *Balaena* and *Grampus* in 1895-1896 wintered at Balaena Bay, three hundred miles east of Herschel, and *Balaena, Beluga, Grampus,* and *Narwhal* went to Langton Bay for the winter of 1897-1898. As it turned out, the ice in these places did not open early enough to give them a clear advantage, so in the following year *Beluga* wintered closer to the 20-25 fathom ground in the small anchorage at Baillie Islands. *Grampus, Narwhal* and James McKenna's *Fearless* would also winter there in 1899-1900. Later, in 1905-1906 and 1907-1908, when the fur trade was as important as whaling, *Olga* wintered on the coast of Victoria Island, the easternmost of the Pacific Arctic wintering sites.[84]

Captain Hartson Bodfish at Baillie Islands, 1899
Old Dartmouth Historical Society
Captain Bodfish, wearing sunglasses, stands near *Beluga*'s stern with a mammoth tusk, found nearby.

Pacific Steam Whaling Company house at Langton Bay, 1910
photograph courtesy of the American Museum of Natural History
Tundra sod has been banked around the house for insulation.

By 1895 the bowheads' major points of congregation throughout the western Arctic had been discovered and exploited. The last of these points and the final retreat of the severely depleted whales was near Cape Bathurst, itself the last important whaling ground to be found by American whalemen. The great returns of baleen to San Francisco—600,000 pounds in 1887, more than 400,000 in 1894—were past, and the productivity of the fishery declined, except for a brief rise in 1898 and 1899.

In retrospect, the season of 1897 marked the beginning of the end. That year, in a major disaster, the ice claimed William Lewis' *Navarch,* the Pacific Steam Whaling Company's *Orca* and *Jesse H. Freeman,* and the schooner *Rosario.* Five other vessels, *Belvedere, Newport, Fearless, Wanderer* and the supply ship *Jeanie* were forced to winter in emergency quarters.[85]

By that time, the Pacific Steam Whaling Company's main investments in the Arctic fishery were five years past. After the purchase of the former coasting steamer *Newport* in 1892, the Company acquired no other ships for whaling. Josiah Knowles, the innovative manager, died in 1896, just as the industry's most profitable days had passed. The directors of the Company may have realized that the stocks of whales were low and that their profits would be more and more determined by luck. In 1896 the Company ended its shore-whaling operations at Point Hope and Point Barrow, and in 1898 and 1899 withdrew its record-holding ships, *Newport* and *Mary D. Hume.*

After the arrival of *Bowhead* (II), itself a late comer in 1898, no large vessel or steamer was entered by any owners in the Arctic fishery. Although the price of baleen remained relatively high—never falling below $2.50 a pound between 1890 and 1897—the scarcity of whales increased the risks of a voyage to the point where large amounts of venture capital were no longer being invested in this "greatest of marine lotteries, the bowhead whale fishery."[86]

By the opening of the twentieth century, whalemen were well aware that accessible new whaling grounds were unlikely to be found in the western Arctic. To maintain profits and to minimize financial risk, the only response that seemed available was to reduce costs by outfitting smaller, less expensive vessels. Although small vessels were by no means rare in the fishery before 1895, their limited capacity prevented them from bringing home large amounts of oil and baleen. Yet as catches declined, large size could be a disadvantage, too. Vessels designed to cart home great quantities of oil and baleen and carry six or seven whaleboats, were costly to operate because of the size of the crew required to man them. *Orca,* for instance, carried about forty-five men, whereas some of the small schooners, introduced near the turn of the century, needed only sixteen or so. Small whalers had their merits, and as their use increased, they came to characterize the last brief phase of the western Arctic fishery.

Equally important as an incentive to use small vessels was the development of the fur trade. From the first opening of the Arctic fishery in 1848, whalemen had traded with Eskimos and Chukchees for Arctic clothing, for furs, and for the baleen from the whales they killed. After 1875, with the price of baleen soaring, the whalers intensified their trading; in the 1890's most ships obtained about seven hundred pounds of traded bone each season, and some took more than three thousand pounds.[87] As baleen catches declined, furs offered a means of offsetting losses from unsuccessful voyages,[88] and the whalemen, now equally proficient as traders, came to rely increasingly on this aspect of their operations in the north.

From 1900 onward, a number of small schooners entered the Arctic for whaling and trading. With small crews, they could hold down their operating costs, trapping and trading during the winter, and if fortunate enough to take a whale or two, then their profits were assured. In 1900 the little 43-ton schooner *Penelope* was fitted out for a two-year whaling voyage, followed by the schooners *Altair* in 1901, *Olga* in 1902, *Bonanza* in 1903 and others, including *Rosie H.* in 1908.

In 1903, William Lewis, the original sponsor of the steam whalers, introduced the last major innovation in the Arctic whale fishery, the use of the internal-combustion engine. The 126-ton schooner *Monterey* was equipped with a small gasoline engine, over the protests of proponents of steam power who claimed, as the sailors had before them, that the engine would be too noisy and would scare the whales.

Orca (left) and *Jesse H. Freeman* (right) shortly before being crushed, 1897.
Private collection

Rosie H. at Baillie Islands, 1917
photograph courtesy of the California Academy of Sciences

Cutting in on *Rosie H.*, 1910
photograph courtesy of the American Museum of Natural History

The small whaling schooners were too light to hoist the headbone from a whale; instead the baleen had to be cut directly from the skull while lines from the vessel lifted the whale partially out of the water.

The voyage was moderately successful. "I found it easier this season to take the few whales we got than under the old methods," said *Monterey*'s master, Captain Foley, because "of her light draught and comparatively small size, [she] could work to better advantage, and the chugging of the engine was no drawback to the work." Sailing skippers told him, he said, that they could hear the steam whalers farther off than they could hear us. "I was able," he continued, "to get a whale that had sounded near an ice pack by simply running through the small openings and meeting him soon after he arose on the opposite side." His opinion, based on experience, was "that the gasoline engine has come to stay in the Arctic whaling business."[89] *Monterey*'s greater maneuverability capitalized on the handicaps of the less agile steamers, just as the first *Mary and Helen* had on those of the sailing vessels twenty years earlier. Three other gasoline auxiliaries were quickly fitted out—*Barbara Hernster, Charles Hanson* and *Olga*—but their whaling returns were small and their profits, if any, must have been based on the fur trade.

The end of the industry occurred, for all intents and purposes, in 1907, when the price of baleen plummeted under the pressure of a new product, spring steel. Within three years, the price fell from $5.00 a pound to less than 50¢. In 1908, the leading Arctic whaling operators—Pacific Steam Whaling Company, William Lewis and Sons, and John A. Cook—withdrew their remaining steam vessels: *Beluga* and *Narwhal, Belvedere* and *William Baylies,* and *Bowhead* (II). In 1909, only the H. Liebes Company's *Herman* and Roth, Blum and Company's *Jeanette* and *Karluk* went north, primarily for the fur trade.

Curiously, the last convulsive lurch of the bowhead fishery took place in New Bedford in 1908, where five years earlier the Old Dartmouth Historical Society had been founded to commemorate the history of the whaling industry. In that year, with the market for baleen collapsed, the remaining whaling companies organized the "whalebone trust" in an effort to force the price of baleen upward. This cartel, run by William Lewis' son, Edgar, received all whalebone imported into the United States and stored it in New Bedford until sold. By doing so, Lewis was able to control the market, such as it was, but for only six years. His last sales were made in 1913 at $1.35 per pound, then he, too, ceased business.[90]

Steam whaling in the western Arctic, a thirty-year episode in the history of American whaling, occurred when a declining industry faced reduced resources and deteriorating markets. The greater efficiency of the steamers brought profits to their owners and the bowheads close to extinction. As the whales became depleted, the price of baleen rose, encouraging the development of cheaper substitutes. Spring steel, when it came, destroyed the baleen market and indirectly saved the bowheads that remained. Beyond questions of the marketplace and the survival of these whales, the age of steam whaling had a further influence, for it and its offspring, the maritime fur trade, ushered in the first commercial development of the western Arctic. In its wake, new ways of life emerged for settlers and Eskimos alike. Profound as these changes were, their endurance is now in question. Before the era of steam whaling was over, Charles Brower, long a resident trader at Point Barrow and onetime employee of the Pacific Steam Whaling Company's station there, discovered the oil seeps in the Sagavanirktok River Delta at Prudhoe Bay.

Monterey
photograph courtesy of the Bancroft Library, University of California

1. I am grateful to Mr. Bernhard Kilian, a participant, for his description of this voyage.

2. Walter S. Tower, *A History of the American Whale Fishery* (Philadelphia, 1907), p. 128.

3. *Ibid.,* p. 129.

4. Computed as yielding 100 barrels (each 31½ gallons) of oil and 1,500 pounds of baleen, with prices from Tower, p. 128.

5. Richard C. Kugler," The Penetration of the Pacific by American Whalemen in the 19th Century," *National Maritime Museum Monographs and Reports,* No. 2 (Greenwich, England, 1971), pp. 20-23.

6. James Templeman Brown, "The Whalemen, Vessels and Boats, Apparatus and Methods of the Whale Fishery," in G. B. Goode, *The Fisheries and Fishery Industries of the United States,* section 5, vol. 2 (Washington, D.C., 1887), p. 236.

7. E. P. Herendeen to W. H. Dall, February 2, 1879, William Healy Dall Papers, Smithsonian Institution Archives, Washington, D.C.

8. Brown, p. 247; Collins, *Report on the Fisheries of The Pacific Coast of the United States* (Washington, D.C., 1891), p. 82.

9. John Bertonccini, "Survivors of the Whaler *Bonanza*," MS, Old Dartmouth Historical Society, New Bedford, Mass.

10. Unidentified newspaper article, Old Dartmouth Historical Society Scrapbook No. 17, p. 10.

11. *Ship Registers of New Bedford, Massachusetts* (Boston: National Archives Project, Works Projects Administration, 1940), vol. 3, pp. 114-115.

12. Reynolds Family Papers, G. W. Blunt White Library, Mystic Seaport, Inc., Mystic, Conn.

13. ODHS Scrapbook No. 17, p. 10.

14. Reynolds Family Papers.

15. *San Francisco Alta California,* April 28, 1883.

16. *San Francisco Daily Bulletin,* October 31, 1883.

17. Michael Jay Mjelde, *Glory of the Seas* (Middletown, Conn., 1970), pp. 32-201 *passim.*

18. *San Francisco Daily Bulletin,* October 31, 1883.

19. Shortly after launching *Thrasher* was rated 1A for fourteen years by an insurance underwriter's survey. ODHS Scrapbook No. 17, p. 57.

20. *San Francisco Alta California,* April 18, 1882; *San Francisco Weekly Bulletin,* March 1, 1882.

21. ODHS Scrapbook No. 17, p. 57; *San Francisco Daily Bulletin,* November 15, 1882.

22. *San Francisco Weekly Bulletin,* November 22, 1882; Donald K. Tressler, *Marine Products of Commerce* (New York, 1923), pp. 635-636.

23. *San Francisco Weekly Bulletin,* April 15, 1891.

24. James Page, *Ice and Ice Movements in Bering Sea during the Spring Months* (Washington, D.C., 1900); Edward Simpson, *Report on Ice and Ice Movements in Bering Sea and the Arctic Basin* (Washington, D.C., 1890).

25. P. F. A. Hegemann, "Das Eis und die Strömungsverhältnisse des Beringmeres, der Beringstrasse und des nördlich davon belegen Eismeeres," *Annalen der Hydrographie und Maritimen Meteorologie,* vol. 18, no. 11 (1890), p. 425.

26. Calvin L. Hooper, *Report of the Cruise of the U.S. Revenue Steamer Corwin* (Washington, D.C., 1881), p. 58.

27. Michael A. Healy, *Report of the Cruise of the Revenue Marine Steamer Corwin* (Washington, D.C., 1889), p. 24.

28. Hegemann, p. 425.

29. Patrick H. Ray, *Report of the International Polar Expedition to Point Barrow, Alaska* (Washington, D.C., 1885), p. 101.

30. *San Francisco Chronicle,* November 16, 1888; Simpson, p. 17.

31. *The Friend* (Honolulu), December 8, 1854.

32. Charles M. Scammon, *The Marine Mammals of the Northwestern Coast of North America* (San Francisco, 1874), p. 65.

33. *San Francisco Weekly Bulletin,* January 30, 1879; *New York Herald,* October 12, 1882.

34. E. P. Herendeen to W. H. Dall, February 2, 1879, William Healy Dall Papers.

35. *San Francisco Chronicle,* July 3, 1889; Charles D. Brower, "The Northernmost American: an Autobiography," undated typescript, U.S. Naval Arctic Research Laboratory, Point Barrow, Alaska, pp. 328-329.

36. *San Francisco Chronicle,* September 30, 1889; Brower, p. 377.

37. The steamers were *Grampus, Lucretia, William Lewis, Jesse H. Freeman, Narwhal, Orca,* and *Thrasher.*

38. Frank Russell, MS journal, April 26, 1893-August 19, 1894, National Anthropological Archives, Smithsonian Institution.

39. *Boston Transcript,* October 6, 1889; *San Francisco Chronicle,* October 30, 1889; Charles H. Stockton, "The Arctic Cruise of the U.S.S. Thetis in the Summer and Autumn of 1889," *National Geographic Magazine,* vol. 2, no. 3 (1890), pp. 183-93.

40. Dorothy Cottle Poole, "Vineyard Whalemen in the Arctic," *Dukes County Intelligencer,* vol. 13, no. 1 (August 1971), pp. 6-7.

41. Matthew Fontaine Maury, *Explanations and Directions to Accompany the Wind and Current Charts,* 5th ed. (Washington, D.C., 1853), pp. 142-143.

42. *San Francisco Weekly Bulletin,* October 4, 1893.

43. *The Alaskan* (Sitka), August 31, 1889; *San Francisco Chronicle,* July 3, 1889 and October 3, 1893.

44. Gilbert Borden, MS journal, 1889-1893, Beinecke Rare Book and Manuscript Library, Yale University, p. 40.

45. *San Francisco Chronicle,* October 3, 1893; Hartson H. Bodfish, *Chasing the Bowhead* (Cambridge, Mass., 1936), p. 47.

46. Bodfish, *Chasing the Bowhead,* pp. 46-47.

47. *San Francisco Weekly Bulletin,* March 16, 1892.

48. Bodfish, *Chasing the Bowhead,* p. 47.

49. Lloyd C. M. Hare, *Salted Tories; The Story of the Whaling Fleet of San Francisco* (Mystic, Conn., 1960), p. 94.

50. Bodfish, *Chasing the Bowhead,* pp. 47-50; Borden, MS journal, p. 61.

51. John A. Cook, *Pursuing the Whale* (Boston, 1926), p. 74.

52. Bodfish, "A Letter Home from Herschel Island—1891," *Dukes County Intelligencer,* vol. 8, no. 3 (February 1967), pp. 57-70.

53. George E. Brandt, "Frozen Toes but not Cold Feet," U.S. Naval Institute *Proceedings,* vol. 55 (1929), pp. 118-120.

54. Bodfish, *Chasing the Bowhead,* p. 49.

55. Bodfish, "A Letter Home from Herschel Island—1891," p. 64.

56. *Ibid.,* p. 70.

57. *Ibid.,* p. 63.

58. *Ibid.*

59. Bodfish, *Chasing the Bowhead,* p. 72.

60. *Ibid.,* p. 82.

61. ODHS Scrapbook No. 16, p. 168.

62. *San Francisco Chronicle,* September 29 and October 1, 1892; ODHS Scrapbook No. 16, p. 168.

63. ODHS Scrapbook No. 16, p. 168.

64. This vessel, the steam brigantine *Jeanette,* has been confused both with the steam bark *Jeannette* (formerly the yacht *Pandora*), which was lost in the ice in the East Siberian Sea in 1881 while on an exploring expedition, and with the ship *Jeannette* of New Bedford, a whaler which operated in the Bering Strait region in the 1850's.

65. Cook, *Pursuing the Whale,* p. 262; Alfred H. Harrison, *In Search of a Polar Continent* (London, 1908), p. 103.

66. Andrew J. Stone, letter quoted in J. A. Allen, "The Musk-oxen of Arctic America and Greenland," *Bulletin of the American Museum of Natural History,* vol. 14 (December 1901), pp. 84-86.

67. Bodfish, *Chasing the Bowhead,* p. 123; Cook, pp. 58, 92.

68. Andrew J. Stone, "Some Results of a Natural History Journey to Northern British Columbia, Alaska, and the Northwest Territory," *Bulletin of the American Museum of Natural History,* vol. 13, no. 5 (1900), p. 57.

69. Bodfish, *Chasing the Bowhead,* p. 136.

70. Bertonccini, "Survivors of the Whaler Bonanza"; Bodfish, *Chasing the Bowhead,* p. 136.

71. Brower, "The Northernmost America," p. 213.

72. Sheldon Jackson, "Education in Alaska, 1892-1893," in *Report of the Commissioner of Education for the Year 1892-93* (Washington, D.C., 1895), p. 1274.

73. Philip H. Godsell, "Pirate Days in Arctic Waters," *Forest and Outdoors,* vol. 37 (1941), pp. 145-146, 152-153.

74. G. B. Ravndal to Secretary of State, June 22, 1906, quoted in R. E. Leet, "American Whalers in the Western Arctic," master's thesis, University of San Francisco, p. 46.

75. Letters, Bishop Reeve to Church Missionary Society, June and August 1894, Church Missionary Society Archives, London.

76. C. E. Whittaker, *Arctic Eskimo* (London, n.d.).

77. Frank A. Peake, *The Bishop Who Ate His Boots; A Biography of Isaac O. Stringer* (Ottawa, 1966), p. 63.

78. Letter, I. O. Stringer to Church Missionary Society, January 10, 1898, Church Missionary Society Archives, London.

79. Peel River and Fort McPherson post reports, Hudson's Bay Company Archives, Winnipeg, Manitoba.

80. Cook, *Pursuing the Whale,* p. 259.

81. John McInnis, MS journal in logbook of the Bark *William Baylies,* December 10, 1894, Nicholson Collection, Providence, R.I., Public Library.

82. Bodfish, *Chasing the Bowhead,* pp. 87-88.

83. *Ibid.,* p. 99.

84. John Bockstoce, "Contacts between American Whalemen and the Copper Eskimos," *Arctic,* vol. 28, no. 4 (December 1975), pp. 298-299.

85. John Bockstoce, "The Arctic Whaling Disaster of 1897," *Prologue; The Journal of the National Archives,* vol. 9, no. 1 (March 1977).

86. ODHS Scrapbook No. 16, p. 218.

87. Moritz Lindeman, *Die Gegenwärtige Eismeer-fischerei und der Walfang* (Berlin, 1899), p. 92.

88. Bodfish, *Chasing the Bowhead,* p. 191.

89. ODHS Scrapbook No. 2, p. 112.

90. ODHS Scrapbook No. T-4, p. 78.

Boats from *Herman* cruising near Cape Bathurst, 1910
photograph courtesy of the American Museum of Natural History

Cruising near Point Barrow, 1911
photograph courtesy of the American Geographical Society
The steering oar is shipped, protruding past the stern.

Cutting in, *Beluga,* 1887

photograph courtesy of New Bedford Free Public Library

The blanket piece is being raised on the cutting tackles at the left, and the whale's lip is being taken up on the right. The men on the cutting stage work with blubber spades as the pieces are raised with the ship's windlass.

Trying out, *Beluga,* 1887

Old Dartmouth Historical Society

After the blubber was brought on board, it was cut into smaller sections known as horse pieces, then minced for faster rendering of the oil. The two men at right work at the mincing horse while another drags a tub of pieces toward the tryworks. To the left of the tryworks is a copper tub in which the oil was cooled before being transferred to wooden casks.

Preparing to take the headbone, *Belvedere, 1912*
photograph courtesy of the American Museum of Natural History
On the whale the man at right uses an axe to disjoint the rostrum from the cranium; at left, another has inserted a chain, the "head strap," through the blow holes.

Hoisting the headbone aboard, *Beluga, 1887*
Old Dartmouth Historical Society

Splitting the headbone, *Herman,* 1917
photograph courtesy of the California Academy of Sciences
Headbone was often split for storage below decks until time was
found to remove the baleen.

Preparing to remove the baleen, *Herman,* 1917
photograph courtesy of the California Academy of Sciences
As time permitted, sections of baleen were cut from the bone.

Scraping the gum from the roots of the baleen
photograph courtesy of Kendall Whaling Museum

Washing bone, schooner *James A. Hamilton*, 1887
photograph courtesy of New Bedford Free Public Library

Cleaning baleen, *Belvedere,* 1912
photograph courtesy of the American Museum of Natural History

Drying baleen, *Belvedere*, 1912
photograph courtesy of the American Museum of Natural History
Before the clean baleen was bundled for storage below decks, it
was dried to prevent mildew. Billy Mogg is at right; his son at left.

The Design and Construction of Steam Whalers

William A. Baker

Mary and Helen

Charles S. Raleigh (1830-1925)

1879, oil on canvas, signed and dated lower left: "C. S. Raleigh, 1879"; 26⅜ x 39⅜ in.

photograph courtesy of the Peabody Museum of Salem

On July 30, 1879, a new vessel was launched into the Kennebec River at Bath, Maine, from the yard of Goss, Sawyer & Packard. Her registered length, breadth, and depth were respectively 138.2 feet, 30.3 feet, and 16.75 feet; she measured 491 tons. Framed of oak and fastened with copper, the vessel's top timbers were of hackmatack, her planking of white oak and yellow pine, while her keelsons, ceiling, and beams were of the best yellow pine. She was painted black with a white streak and was bark-rigged, spreading 2,850 yards of canvas. In her topgallant forecastle this new bark carried two donkey engines for handling anchors and cargo.

The vessel was a whaler and the description, as far as it goes, could have applied to many of the barks built at Bath in the 1870's and 1880's. There was something different about her, however, for between her main and mizzen masts there was a black smokestack and in an aperture forward of her rudder there was a propeller. This new bark—the first steam whaler to be built and registered in the United States—was the *Mary and Helen,* built for Captain William Lewis of New Bedford, probably from a model cut by William Potter Pattee, Bath's noted ship designer.

Mary and Helen was really an auxiliary steamer, for she carried full sail power, a bark rig with royals on fore and main masts, which was employed when making passages. Her single-cylinder engine and boiler came from the Delamater Iron Works of New York City. She could stow two hundred tons of coal which, augmented by blubber scraps from her tryworks, was considered sufficient fuel for a year. *Mary and Helen* was unusual in another respect—she carried two figures representing her sponsors, the Misses Haskell of New Bedford. The famous Colonel C. A. L. Sampson of Bath carved a figure of Mary for the bow and one of Helen for the stern.

On Friday, August 24, 1879, one hour after the fires were lighted, steam was on in *Mary and Helen's* boiler for the first time. Under the command of Captain Lewis and with a number of prominent shipbuilders on board, she had her trial trip up and down the Kennebec in front of Bath.

According to the local newspaper, "she made about eight knots an hour, and steered splendidly, almost obeying the slightest impulse of the wheelsman."

Four days after launching, *Mary and Helen* left Bath for New Bedford to complete her outfitting. By September 12, she was ready for sea, and under the command of Captain M. V. B. Millard, the new whaler sailed from New Bedford, bound for the Arctic Ocean via the Hawaiian Islands. She had storage for 2,700 barrels of oil and carried four working boats with three in reserve. Costs of construction and outfitting were estimated at $65,000. Steam whalers reportedly cost about three times as much as sailing whalers of the same capacity; crew costs were also higher because of the need to employ several trained engineers.

Henry Hall noted in his 1882 *Report on the Ship-Building Industry of the United States* that the introduction of steam-propelled vessels into the United States whaling fleet was in imitation of the Canadians who during the previous fifteen years had transformed most of their fleet to steamers. The English sent the first steam whalers to sea in 1857, *Diana* of Hull and *Tay* of Dundee, both sailing vessels to which auxiliary steam power was added. Others were built or converted in succeeding years; most were of wood, the favored material following the loss of three iron steamers. The entire Dundee fleet of whalers had steam power by 1869.

The first auxiliary steamer in the American whaling fleet was the 212-ton bark *Pioneer* of New London, a former government transport in which steam machinery was installed in 1865. She made a successful voyage to Davis Strait between April and November 1866, but in her second Arctic season she was crushed by ice and abandoned in July 1867. The steam brig *Siberia* was built on the Pacific coast in the late 1870's for whaling in Russian waters. Although owned primarily by the Americans and having an American master, she flew the Russian flag, thus giving to *Mary and Helen* her unique status as the first steam whaler built and registered in the United States.

The *Charles W. Morgan,* launched in New Bedford in 1841 and now preserved afloat at Mystic Seaport, might be called the classic sailing whaleship, the type reputedly built by the mile and cut off as needed. She has full bows, considerable deadrise, a moderately rounded bilge, and a long, relatively fine run. For the shapes of sailing whalers other than the *Morgan*, models and photographs are the only evidence.

During the peak of the clipper ship era, say 1850-1853, almost every ship that loaded for California was advertised as at least a half-clipper. Bow and stern profiles similar to those of clipper ships could be found on even the full-bodied ships built during the 1850's. Although there was no great need for speed by a vessel that spent a large part of her time cruising under shortened sail, the builders of large whaling vessels launched during the second half of the nineteenth century followed the fashion and gave their products finer bows with clipper ship profiles. The deadrise, run, and transom stern, however, differed but little from those of the *Charles W. Morgan*. The so-called clipper whalers actually bore more resemblance to the China packets of the 1840's than to the clippers of the 1850's.

The raking stems of the clipper whalers, it has been claimed, made them better performers in ice fields than the older types of sailing whalers. Their sharper bows might have opened ice leads better than the rounded bow of the *Morgan* but as long as Arctic whalers depended entirely on sail for propulsion they had no real ice-breaking ability. Once in the Arctic, they could not transship their oil and bone, and thus required a larger than normal cargo capacity in relation to their size. Some speed, on the other hand, was desired to reduce the time needed to reach the whaling grounds.

Ideally, a vessel intended for Arctic work should be so shaped that when caught in the ice she would be lifted out rather than crushed. A ship having considerable deadrise—a wedge-shaped bottom—would have this quality; she would also be faster under sail but a poorer carrier than one with a more normal form. Perhaps the best known vessel built for ice work was Fridtjof Nansen's *Fram*, designed by Colin Archer of Larvik, Norway, in 1891. The *Fram*, frozen in the ice, drifted in the Arctic for twenty-two months with no damage, completely confounding the skeptics. She was, of course, too late to affect the design of steam whalers in the United States where, in view of the conflicting requirements stated above, shipbuilders continued to produce heavily-built, normal form hulls capable of withstanding some ice pressure.

Masters of vessels engaged in Arctic whaling had to try to keep from getting caught in ice; if caught, the vessels were usually lost by crushing or grounding. Nearly every year one or more whalers were lost. The great disasters occurred in 1871 when thirty-one vessels went down and in 1876 when another twelve were crushed. The early steam whalers required the same conflicting qualities as the sailing whalers, for with low-powered engines and restricted fuel supplies

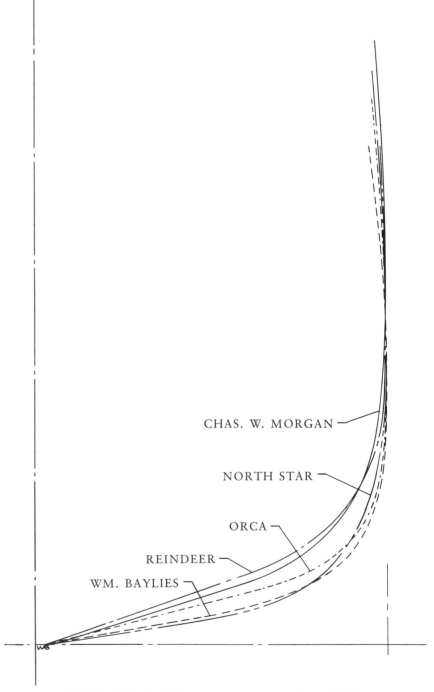

CHAS. W. MORGAN

NORTH STAR

ORCA

REINDEER

WM. BAYLIES

COMPARATIVE MIDSECTIONS
THREE SAILING AND TWO STEAM WHALERS

Builder's half-model, bark *William Baylies*

1886, lift construction, pine and mahogany; length of model: 63¾ in.

Old Dartmouth Historical Society

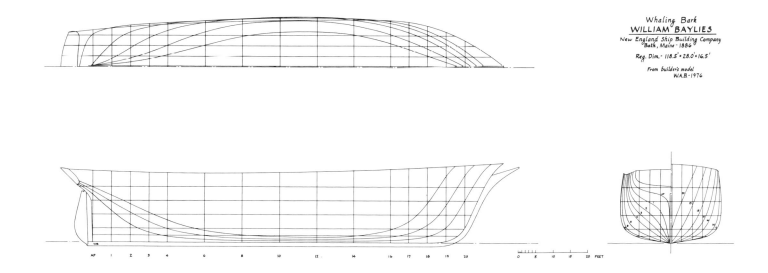

Whaling Bark
WILLIAM BAYLIES
New England Ship Building Company
Bath, Maine · 1886
Reg. Dim. · 118.5' × 28.0' × 16.5'

From builder's model
W.A.B·1976

Builder's half-model, *North Star*
Probably carved by William Potter Pattee, 1880
Old Dartmouth Historical Society

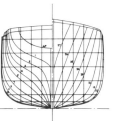

Steam Whaling Bark
NORTH STAR
Goss, Sawyer & Packard
Bath, Maine - 1881
Reg. Dim. - 138.3' x 31.4' x 16.6'

From builder's model
W.A.B. - 1976

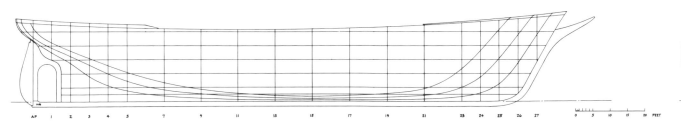

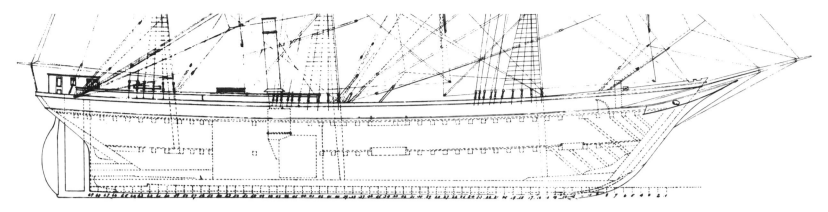

Hull profile of *Bowhead*

Plans dated October 8, 1890, probably from files of Union Iron Works, San Francisco

photograph courtesy of Mystic Seaport

A few details of *North Star*'s structure and finish taken from a contemporary newspaper may be considered typical of the Bath-built steam whalers:

She is most thoroughly constructed after the same model as the *Belvedere,* with framework and planking of white oak, and is solidly braced with hanging and standing knees, the lower pointers reaching as far aft as the forward hatch. Forward she is built solid for a distance of 20 feet and 6 feet in height with yellow pine timbers laid lengthwise and securely bolted together. She is ceiled six inches in thickness inside, the oak planking is 6 inches in thickness, and in addition she has 3½ inch oak sheathing on the bow and has an iron shoe ⅜ of an inch thick on her stem. She has a double planksheer and solidly built rail 4 feet 8 inches in height.

The after cabin is very handsomely fitted, the wood being of curly and birdseye maple, the door panels of French laurel, pilasters of mahogany, coving of rosewood, and other parts inlaid with black walnut and gilt, and the ceiling is painted white. The furniture of this cabin is in harmony with the general fittings, and on the floor is a tapestry carpet of subdued hues. The main cabin is ceiled [sheathed] with ash and ornamented with much the same kind of woods as the after cabin. In the centre is the officers' dining table and on the floor is an oil-cloth carpet. The ceiling is painted white. On the starboard side doors open into the pantry and rooms of the first and second mates. The staterooms are neatly furnished, and the pantry is finished in black walnut, while the cabins are well lighted by skylights. In the forward part of the house are the rooms of the boatsteerers, steward and assistant engineer, with the galley in the extreme front. There are two decks to the steamer, and the forecastle provides ample accommodation, well lighted and ventilated for the crew.

The money-making capabilities of the steam whalers from Bath were not lost on San Francisco whaleship owners who could not understand why Arctic whaling out of the Golden Gate should be controlled from New Bedford, three thousand miles away. Two of them, Captain Charles Goodall and George Clement Perkins, formed Goodall, Perkins & Company, which contracted for a steam whaler for the 1882 season with the Dickie Brothers, Scottish shipbuilders whose yard was located in the Potrero district. The result was the *Bowhead* launched at one hour past midnight on April 12, 1882. She had her trial trip on April 26 and sailed for the Arctic at 3:00 A.M. on April 27.

Bowhead was followed by *Orca, Narwhal,* and *Balaena,* all from the Dickie Brothers' yard, and *Thrasher* built by Goss, Sawyer & Packard at Bath. Associated with Goodall and Perkins in the building of these vessels were Captain Millen Griffith, a tugboat owner, and Captain Josiah N. Knowles, who had served as agent for Captain Lewis at San Francisco. According to newspaper accounts, the owners of the steam whalers varied but usually included two or more of these four men. On October 30, 1883, they formed a new corporation, the Pacific Steam Whaling Company, which

they were primarily sailing vessels. While considered to be the perfection of model—strong vessels of good sailing lines and good carriers—they were no better than the bluff-bowed sailing ships when once caught in the ice. The steam bark *North Star,* for example, was crushed on July 8, 1882, on her maiden voyage.

Among the vessels lost in the disaster of 1871 was ship *Reindeer,* built in Mattapoisett, Massachusetts, in 1853 and one of the fastest and finest sailing whalers of her day. *Reindeer's* features were quite similar to those of the China packet *Montauk,* which was built by William H. Webb in 1844, then served as a whaler in the 1850's. *Reindeer* had about five degrees more deadrise than the *Montauk* and the entrance angle of her load waterline was about five degrees sharper. Both *Reindeer* and *Montauk* were narrower in proportion to length than the *Morgan.* In Table I the basic features of the *Charles W. Morgan, Reindeer, Montauk,* and the *William Baylies,* a whaling bark built at Bath in 1886, are compared.

TABLE I	CHARLES W. MORGAN	MONTAUK	REINDEER	WILLIAM BAYLIES
	1841	1844	1853	1886
Registered length	105.6'	128.0'	123.5'	118.5'
Registered breadth	27.7'	29.5'	28.3'	28.0'
Length/breadth	3.81	4.34	4.37	4.24
Deadrise	18°	14°	19½°	10°
Entrance angle	70°	38°	33°	37°

On October 10, 1880, *Mary and Helen* returned to San Francisco from her first Arctic voyage with a cargo of oil and bone that grossed over $100,000. Because of her success in the ice, she was purchased by the federal government for use in the search for the exploring vessel *Jeannette,* which had sailed on July 8, 1879, to seek out a possible route to the Pole from Wrangel Island. Before she left San Francisco under her new name of U.S.S. *Rodgers,* Captain Lewis's second steam whaler, *Belvedere,* had been launched at Bath by Goss, Sawyer & Packard. She was followed in 1881 by *North Star* from the same yard; then by the second *Mary and Helen* in 1882. Captain Lewis had two other steam whalers built at Bath, both by Kelley, Spear & Company, the *William Lewis* in 1888 and the *Navarch* in 1892. The registered dimensions and gross tonnages of these Bath-built steam whalers are given in Table II.

TABLE II New Bedford-owned Steam Whalers REGISTERED DIMENSIONS	LENGTH	BREADTH	DEPTH	GROSS TONS
1879 *Mary and Helen* (I)	138.2'	30.3'	16.75'	491
1880 *Belvedere*	140.6'	31.3'	17.2'	440
1881 *North Star*	138.3'	31.4'	16.6'	489
1882 *Mary and Helen* (II)	141.8'	31.3'	16.7'	508
1888 *William Lewis*	134.0'	30.0'	16.55'	463
1892 *Navarch*	142.8'	31.1'	16.8'	494

In spite of the apparent differences in dimensions and tonnages all six were probably built from the same model, which very likely was cut by Bath's premier designer, William Potter Pattee. Some of the differences, particularly in length and depth, can be attributed to the almost impossible task of trying to build identical wooden vessels. A minute change in the angle of the keel-stem scarf can result in a considerable difference in the length measured at deck level some twenty feet above.

William Pattee is known to have designed *Belvedere* and there is published material indicating that *North Star* and *Navarch* were built from the same model. There is also a published statement that the second *Mary and Helen* was "a counterpart of her predecessor" which could have been either *North Star* or the first *Mary and Helen.* Another account mentions that the second *Mary and Helen* was built to nearly the same model as the first *Mary and Helen* but with ninety tons more capacity. This points to *North Star* as the predecessor and explains the additional foot of breadth that appeared in *Belvedere.*

The 30.0 foot breadth of the *William Lewis* is not easily explained. Goss, Sawyer & Packard failed in 1883 but the firm's successor, the New England Ship Building Company, the builder of the *William Baylies* in 1886 and perhaps the logical builder of the *Lewis,* was active in 1888 and William Pattee was still in business. It seems as though the new builder—Kelley, Spear & Company—had obtained and used the moulds of the first *Mary and Helen,* not knowing that one foot had been added to the maximum breadth of her successors. When Kelley, Spear built *Navarch* in 1892, the one foot was added.

When the first *Mary and Helen* was built in 1879 she was said to have been designed with a somewhat fuller form than the sailing whalers built at Bath in the 1870's because the weight of her steam machinery would reduce her carrying capacity. She was, however, proportionately narrower than any of the vessels in Table I, having a length-breadth ratio of 4.57. Steam power proved so useful when working through the ice fields that the reduction in carrying capacity was accepted when two Bath-built sailing whalers had steam propelling plants installed, *Lucretia* of 1877, converted in 1881, and the *William Baylies* in the early 1890's. By this time, with catches smaller and oil prices lower, a ship's capacity may not have been important.

Plans exist for the U.S.S. *Rodgers,* ex-*Mary and Helen,* showing her as strengthened for her rescue mission. The lines plan was drawn to the outside of tapering sheathing and planking, making it difficult to work back to her designed form, but her deadrise was about 8° and her entrance angle 28°. The lines of *North Star,* taken from a half-model probably carved for display after her completion but close enough for comparison purposes, shows the deadrise to be 8½° and the entrance angle 28°.

William Lewis
Charles S. Raleigh (1830-1925)
1888, oil on canvas, signed and dated lower left: "C. S. Raleigh 1888"; 26½ x 39¾ in.
photograph courtesy of Kendall Whaling Museum

Sail plan for *North Star* and *Belvedere*
1880, Briggs and Beckman Sail Loft, New Bedford
courtesy of the John Carter Brown Library, Brown University

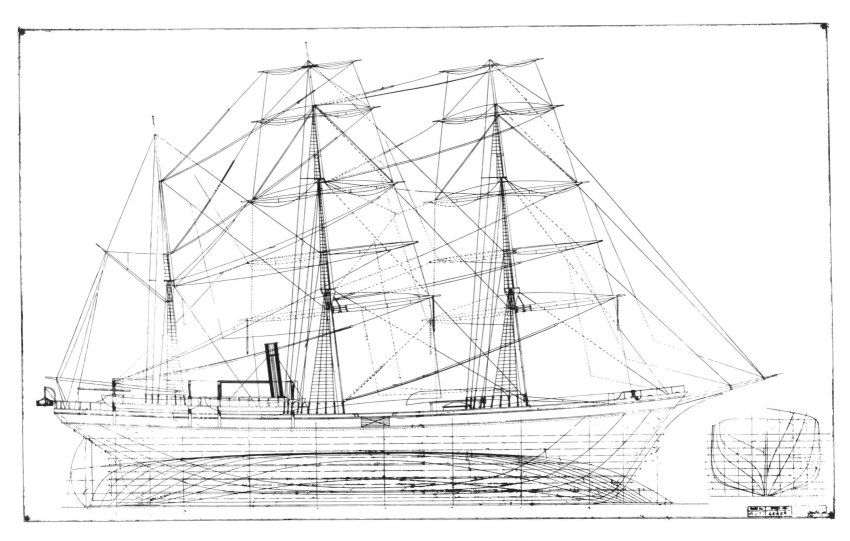

Lines and sail plan of *Orca*
From Union Iron Works files, dated April 2, 1892
Old Dartmouth Historical Society, gift of William A. Baker

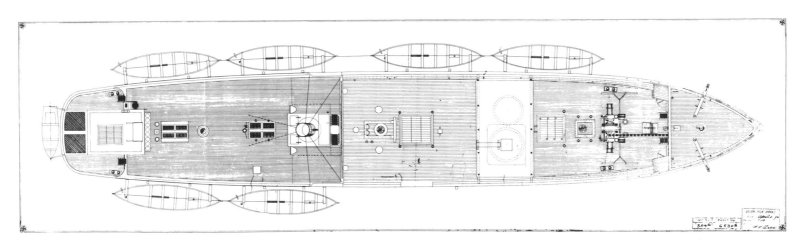

Deck layout of *Orca*
Plans from Union Iron Works files, dated April 2, 1892
Old Dartmouth Historical Society, gift of William A. Baker

Rigged model, *Orca*

ca. 1882; overall height 70¾ in., length 108⅛ in.

Old Dartmouth Historical Society: model lent by the Museum of History and Technology, Smithsonian Institution

took ownership of these vessels and others that had been purchased. The registered dimensions and tonnages of the San Francisco-built steam whalers and *Thrasher* are given in Table III.

TABLE III   San Francisco-owned Steam Whalers

REGISTERED DIMENSIONS

	NAME	LENGTH	BREADTH	DEPTH	GROSS TONS
1882	*Bowhead*	175'	31'	17.9'	533
1882	*Orca*	177.0'	32.5'	18.9'	628
1883	*Narwhal*	149.5'	32.0'	17.0'	524
1883	*Balaena*	149.5'	32.0'	17.0'	524
1883	*Thrasher*	144.7'	31.5'	16.4'	512

Orca, the largest of the four San Francisco-built steam whalers, is the only one for which a lines plan is currently available. Her form was similar to that of the Bath-built steamers but she had more deadrise, $14\frac{1}{2}°$, and to compensate for this her waterlines were fuller, the entrance angle being $31°$. She was also relatively narrower, her length/breadth ratio being 5.45.

The Bath-built steam whalers for Captain William Lewis followed the lead of the first *Mary and Helen* in having single cylinder engines. Hers measured 22 by 28 inches and developed 250 horsepower; engines of the same size built by the Delamater Iron Works of New York were fitted in *Belvedere* and *North Star*. The new Bath Iron Works built a 22 by 36 inch, 320-horsepower engine for *Navarch* as well as her boiler and all auxiliaries.

The steam whalers built at San Francisco had more sophisticated machinery. *Bowhead* had compound engines with cylinders 12 and 34 inches in diameter and a 28-inch stroke, while *Balaena* was said to have had the first set of triple-expansion engines constructed in the United States. They were built by the Risdon Iron Works, located near the Dickie shipyard. The fuel economy of the triple-expansion engines seemed an obvious advantage to a whaler on a long voyage. Captain Lewis and the Bath people, however, believed that the simplicity of the single engine was to be preferred over the fuel economy of the more complicated power plants.

The Bath-built steam whalers had fixed two-bladed propellers that could be aligned with their stern posts to reduce drag when under sail. *Bowhead*, however, had a two-bladed propeller in a frame which, when proceeding under sail, could be disconnected from the shaft and hoisted clear of the water. The propeller aperture was then filled with what was called a "centerboard" of wood. *Orca* also had a hoisting propeller but the sister ships *Narwhal* and *Balaena* did not.

The San Francisco-built *Orca, Balaena,* and *Narwhal* and the Bath-built *Thrasher* introduced built-in iron tanks for the whale oil, a new feature that was adopted to eliminate the need to cool the oil before running it into the usual wooden casks. With iron tanks the oil could be run in hot, saving both time and the loss of oil. It was estimated that a 400-ton ship with tanks could carry the same amount of oil as a 600-ton ship using wooden casks. These vessels also carried steam tryworks. *Thrasher*'s was designed by Frank Reynolds of New York, who had been engineer on the *Mary and Helen* and whose brother, George Reynolds, had made and installed the engine on the *Pioneer*.

So successful were the specially-built steam whalers that some sailing whalers had power added, while other vessels with auxiliary or full steam power were adapted for Arctic whaling for one or more voyages. These vessels, varying so much in hull characteristics and power and coming to the business as it was dying, had no influence on design. Actually, they were a rather strange assortment to be engaged in whaling; power was wanted and almost any type of hull would do.

Belvedere at San Francisco, about 1903
courtesy of Bath Marine Museum

Belvedere's bow carvings
courtesy of Bath Marine Museum

Beluga, formerly *Mary and Helen* (II), at San Francisco,
about 1905
courtesy of San Francisco Maritime Museum

PACIFIC Steam Whaling Company.

J. N. KNOWLES, MANAGER.

EDWIN L. GRIFFITH, SECRETARY.

OFFICE, 28 CALIFORNIA ST.

San Francisco, 31st Dec/94

Ship Biographies

John R. Bockstoce

The vessels described below are grouped under three headings: the class of steam whalers, other steamers entered in the fishery, and gasoline whalers. Within each category vessels are arranged alphabetically. For each vessel, its gross tonnage, dimensions, rig, and horsepower are given, drawn for the most part from information contained in the Bureau of Navigation's yearly *List of Merchant Vessels of the United States* and from the *Record of American and Foreign Shipping,* published annually by the American Bureau of Shipping in New York. Occasionally, contemporary newspaper accounts have been relied on for information not elsewhere available. Logbooks and journals of specific voyages, if available in public collections, have been identified, using the following abbreviations to designate the institution that holds them:

BLHU Baker Library, Harvard University
CAS California Academy of Sciences, San Francisco
DCHS Dukes County Historical Society, Edgartown, Massachusetts
IMA International Marine Archives, Nantucket, Massachusetts
KWM Kendall Whaling Museum, Sharon, Massachusetts
MSI Mystic Seaport Incorporated, Mystic, Connecticut
NHA Nantucket (Massachusetts) Historical Association
ODHS Old Dartmouth Historical Society, New Bedford, Massachusetts
PPL Providence (Rhode Island) Public Library
SCS Southampton (New York) Colonial Society

Balaena at San Francisco, 1883
photograph courtesy of San Francisco Maritime Museum

BALAENA

TONNAGE: 524

DIMENSIONS: 149.5' x 32' x 17'

RIG: bark

HORSEPOWER: 245

Like her sister ship *Narwhal*, *Balaena* was built in San Francisco during the winter of 1882-1883 by Dickie Brothers for the Pacific Steam Whaling Company. She made fourteen voyages—all to the Arctic and four of them wintering voyages—before being lost on the south coast of St. Lawrence Island in a gale on June 7, 1901. She took sixty-seven whales on her voyage of 1892-1894, the second largest catch, after *Narwhal*'s sixty-nine, of any steam whaler.

MANUSCRIPT ACCOUNTS:

Voyage of 1883-1884: incomplete journal kept by G. F. Bauldry, master (IMA). *Voyage of 1901:* journal kept by G. B. Leavitt, master (BLHU).

Belvedere at Seattle, 1913
photograph courtesy of San Francisco Maritime Museum

Belvedere at Petropavlovsk, Kamchatka, 1913
photograph courtesy of Bernhard Kilian

BELVEDERE

TONNAGE: 440

DIMENSIONS: 140.6′ x 31.3′ x 17.2′

RIG: bark

HORSEPOWER: 45

Belvedere was launched at Bath, Maine, in July 1880. Her maiden voyage, under Captain Leander Owen, was very successful: she took 600 walrus, fourteen bowheads, and some sperm whales, arriving in San Francisco in November 1881 with 1800 barrels of bowhead oil, 34,000 pounds of baleen, and 2500 pounds of walrus ivory. While on the voyage she obtained the first news of the loss of the U.S.S. *Rodgers* (ex-*Mary and Helen*) and was the second vessel to land a boat on Wrangel Island.

Belvedere served in the whaling trade longer than any other steamer, making twenty-five voyages from San Francisco before being sold to Seattle in 1913. William Lewis and Sons retired her from whaling after the 1908 season, and she lay idle until Captain Stephen Cottle arranged for her purchase in early 1911. Thereafter, she was in the Arctic each year, but primarily as a trader and freighter. In 1913 Hibbard-Stewart Company of Seattle, fur dealers, purchased *Belvedere*, and she sailed from that port until 1919, when she was crushed in the ice near Cape Serdze Kamen, Siberia.

MANUSCRIPT ACCOUNTS:

Voyage of 1883-1884: logbook kept by J. M. McLane, chief officer (DCHS); incomplete journal kept by G. F. Smith, master (DCHS). *Voyage of 1884-1885*: logbook kept by C. H. Tucker, chief officer (ODHS); incomplete journal kept by G. F. Smith, master (DCHS). *Voyage of 1889-1890*: logbook (ODHS). *Voyage of 1894-1896*: incomplete journal (PPL). *Voyage of 1897-1898*: logbook (ODHS); incomplete journal kept by M. V. B. Millard (ODHS). *Voyage of 1904*: journal (PPL). *Voyage of 1907*: journal (KWM). *Voyage of 1908*: logbook kept by W. F. Joseph, chief officer (DCHS).

Bowhead at San Francisco with baleen drying in shrouds
photograph courtesy of San Francisco Maritime Museum

BOWHEAD (I)

TONNAGE: 533
DIMENSIONS: 175' x 31' x 17.9'
RIG: bark
HORSEPOWER: nominal 280

The first of the class of steam whalers to be built on the Pacific coast, *Bowhead* was launched from the Dickie Brothers yard in San Francisco in 1882. Strongly built, she had a heavy oak stem and stern post, oak sheathing, planking of Oregon pine, and ¾-inch iron plates on her bow. Pointers and crossbeams were used to reinforce her forward parts. Her spars were made by the Charles Castner Company of San Francisco.

Bowhead was equipped with a compound, surface-condensing engine built by the Risdon Iron Works and steam-powered windlass and winches. Her boiler was 11 feet 6 inches in diameter and 11 feet long. The windlass and winches were intended for use not only in cutting-in, working sails, and pumping, but also for raising the propeller, which was perhaps her most innovative feature. Because speed under sail was desired when making passages, her propeller shaft, like *Orca*'s, was designed so that it could be withdrawn from the hub and then the two-bladed, 9 foot 6 inch propeller could be hoisted into the ship in a sliding frame. A centerboard was then placed in the space to increase the ease of handling when under sail.

Bowhead made three voyages, all to the Arctic, under the experienced master, Captain E. Everett Smith, who had earlier commanded the Russian-registered steam brig *Siberia*. Her first two voyages were successful. While on her third, she made fast to grounded ice near Icy Cape on August 11, 1884, to clean her boilers. Struck and holed by a piece of drifting ice, she sank quickly. The crew made their way to *Narwhal* and *Balaena* nearby.

U.S.S. *Rodgers,* formerly *Mary and Helen,* at San Francisco, 1881
photograph courtesy of U.S. Navy

MARY AND HELEN (I)

TONNAGE: 490.50
DIMENSIONS: 138.2′ x 30.3′ x 16.7′
RIG: bark
HORSEPOWER: nominal 90

Mary and Helen, the first of the class of steam whalers, was built in 1879 at Bath, Maine, by Goss, Sawyer & Packard. Designed for Arctic work, she was strengthened for ice and had a power plant capable of driving her at about eight knots. Her boiler, according to the *New York Herald* of February 24, 1881, "was horizontal, with return tubes, carrying from 35 to 40 pounds of steam. Coal bunkers store 150 tons and with continual fire she consumes about five tons each twenty-four hours." She was also fitted with two auxiliary donkey engines for her windlass and winches.

Mary and Helen sailed for Hawaii, using steam power to pass through the Straits of Magellan rather than battle Cape Horn. In Honolulu, Captain Leander Owen assumed command for her only Arctic whaling voyage. She returned to San Francisco in November 1880 with oil and baleen that brought $100,000 to her owners, an amount considerably greater than the $65,000 it had cost to build and outfit her.

Early in 1881, the United States Government purchased *Mary and Helen* for $100,000, renamed her U.S.S. *Rodgers,* and sent her out in search of the missing *Jeannette* Arctic expedition. On November 30, 1881, while frozen in at St. Lawrence Bay, Siberia, she burned to the waterline. The crew was forced to spend the winter ashore, living with natives.

MANUSCRIPT ACCOUNTS:
Voyage of 1879-1880: logbook (ODHS); journal kept by I. H. Reynolds, assistant engineer (MSI); incomplete journal kept by B. F. Reynolds, chief engineer (MSI).

Mary and Helen (II)

Charles S. Raleigh, 1830-1925

1882, oil on canvas, signed and dated lower left: "C. S. Raleigh, 1882"; 27 x 40 in.

Old Dartmouth Historical Society, gift of Mrs. Andrew G. Pierce, Jr., 1915

Beluga at Dutch Harbor
Private collection

MARY AND HELEN (II) later BELUGA

TONNAGE: 508

DIMENSIONS: 141.8′ x 31.3′ x 16.7′

RIG: bark

HORSEPOWER: 297

Immediately after the sale of the first *Mary and Helen*, William Lewis began construction of the second. Built in Bath by Goss, Sawyer & Packard, she was outfitted in New Bedford and sailed for the Pacific in August 1882. After one voyage to the Arctic, Lewis sold her, having suffered a major financial loss when his *North Star* was crushed by ice in July 1882.

Mary and Helen (II) made three voyages for her new owners, the Pacific Steam Whaling Company, before being heavily damaged by fire while at San Francisco in December 1886. Her insurers declared her a total loss and paid the Company's claim. The Company then repurchased the hulk for five hundred dollars and rebuilt it, naming the largely new vessel *Beluga*. Fourteen voyages—four of them with winterings—followed before *Beluga* was withdrawn from whaling in 1908. She appears to have lain idle in Oakland Estuary until the outbreak of World War I, when she was put into service as a freighter. While carrying benzine and gasoline to Australia, she was sunk by the German raider *Wolf* off Fanning Island in July 1917.

MANUSCRIPT ACCOUNTS:

Voyage of 1884-1885: journal kept by F. A. Barker, master (ODHS). *Voyage of 1886*: journal kept by F. A. Barker, master (NHA). *Voyage of 1893*: journal kept by J. G. Baker, master (PPL).

Narwhal at San Francisco, 1883
photograph courtesy of San Francisco Maritime Museum

NARWHAL

TONNAGE: 524
DIMENSIONS: 149.5′ x 32′ x 17′
RIG: bark
HORSEPOWER: 245

The steam whaler with the longest record of service, *Narwhal* was built with her sister ship, *Balaena,* at the Dickie Brothers yard in San Francisco in the winter of 1882-1883. Before she was withdrawn from whaling in 1908, she made seventeen voyages to the Arctic, wintered on five of them, and on one, from 1892-1894, took sixty-nine whales, and set a record for steam whalers. After her whaling days were over, she served as a salmon packer, then was sold to Warner Brothers Pictures and appeared as the *Pequod* in the 1922 version of *Moby-Dick*. In 1931, *Narwhal* was sold to Mexico and disappears from the record.

MANUSCRIPT ACCOUNTS:
Voyage of 1897-1898: journal kept by J. A. Tilton, master (DCHS). *Voyage of 1902-1904:* journal kept by G. B. Leavitt, master (BLHU). *Voyage of 1905-1907:* journal kept by G. B. Leavitt, master (BLHU). *Voyage of 1908:* journal kept by G. B. Leavitt, master (BLHU).

Navarch at Bath, 1892
photograph courtesy of Bath Marine Museum

NAVARCH

TONNAGE: 494

DIMENSIONS: 142.8' x 31.1' x 16.8'

RIG: bark

HORSEPOWER: 400 (estimated)

Navarch, the last of the class of steam whalers built in the United States, was launched in Bath, Maine, in 1892 for William Lewis. She made only three Arctic voyages, none outstanding. Caught in the ice off Blossom Shoals in August 1897, she was abandoned by her crew, sixteen of whom died marching over the ice to shore. *Navarch* drifted in the ice near Point Barrow until January 1898, when she was set on fire by salvagers.

MANUSCRIPT ACCOUNTS:

Voyage of 1892-1893: logbook kept by E. P. Sampson (ODHS). *Voyage of 1893-1896:* logbook, probably kept by J. G. Belain, first mate (ODHS). *Voyage of 1897:* logbook, probably kept by J. G. Belain, first mate, then by T. Birnbaum, seaman (ODHS).

North Star

Charles S. Raleigh, 1830-1925

1880, oil on canvas, signed and dated lower left. "C. S. Raleigh 180"; 20½ x 39½ in.

photograph courtesy of Kendall Whaling Museum

NORTH STAR

TONNAGE: 489

DIMENSIONS: 138.3′ x 31.4′ x 16.6′

RIG: bark

HORSEPOWER: nominal 100

North Star was built at Bath in 1881 and arrived in Honolulu in March 1882 to prepare for her Arctic cruise under the command of Captain Leander Owen. Reaching St. Lawrence Bay in June, she rescued the shipwrecked crew of the U.S.S. *Rodgers,* but later in the season she met her own fate. Owen's belief in the advantages of steam power may have led him to overestimate its potential, for he worked his way far into the Arctic in advance of the rest of the fleet. *North Star* reached the Sea Horse Islands, eighty miles southwest of Point Barrow on June 25, the earliest date any vessel is known to have done so. As the pack ice descended, Owen took the vessel farther north, hoping to find protection behind the great pressure ridge always found near Point Barrow. On July 8, however, *North Star* was crushed near the Point, about two-and-a-half miles from shore. The force of the ice was so great that the cracking of her timbers could be heard on shore, and her engineer, Frank Reynolds, reported that "the ship was ground as fine as matches." The crew made their way over the ice to safety at the U.S. Army's Signal Service Station.

MANUSCRIPT ACCOUNT:

Voyage of 1881-1882: logbook (ODHS).

Orca at San Francisco, 1882
photograph courtesy of San Francisco Maritime Museum

ORCA

TONNAGE: 628

DIMENSIONS: 177′ x 32.5′ x 18.9′

RIG: bark

HORSEPOWER: nominal 280

The largest of the class of steam whalers, *Orca* was built immediately after *Bowhead* had been launched and shared many of the design features of *Bowhead* and carried seven boats. *Orca,* however, had two new features, a steam digester for trying out oil and iron tanks for storing it.

Her fifteen Arctic voyages were largely successful and often eventful. On October 22-23, 1883, she was overtaken north of Bering Strait by a terrific gale and lost "her smokestacks, steam launch, skiff, and five whaleboats," as "heavy seas swept every moveable thing on deck overboard." The next year she added a thousand dollars to her owners' profits by towing the *Abraham Barker,* a sailing bark, from a dangerous position in the pack ice near Point Barrow. In 1887, on a voyage when she took a season's record of twenty-eight whales, she towed the seventeen-ton whaling sloop *Spy* to Point Barrow for use in lagoon whaling by the Pacific Steam Whaling Company's shore station. She set another record on July 4, 1888, by running up a wide lane of open water and reaching Point Barrow nearly a month before the usual date. After dropping off two boat crews for whaling in the leads, she immediately retreated to the south, but was nearly lost near Icy Cape when the pack closed in on her.

Orca was lost in September 1897 when trying to escape the rapidly closing ice near the Sea Horse Islands. Shortly before, she had rescued the crew of the trapped *Jesse H. Freeman,* only to be fatally nipped a few hours later. George Fred Tilton described her end: "Orca was caught between two immense ice floes and crushed with such force as to take the stern post and steering gear completely out of her and hurl the wheel through the pilot house."

MANUSCRIPT ACCOUNTS:

Voyage of 1886: incomplete journal kept by G. F. Bauldry, master (IMA). *Voyage of 1891:* logbook kept by T. P. Warren (IMA). *Voyage of 1897:* logbook kept by T. P. Warren (SCS).

Thrasher fitting out at New Bedford, 1883
Old Dartmouth Historical Society

THRASHER

TONNAGE: 512

DIMENSIONS: 144.7′ x 31.5′ x 16.4′

RIG: bark

HORSEPOWER: 373

Thrasher, the only vessel built for the Pacific Steam Whaling Company on the east coast, was launched at Bath in 1883. Fitted out in New Bedford, she arrived in December of the same year in San Francisco. From 1884 to 1908, *Thrasher* made twenty-one voyages to the Arctic, wintering over twice. In 1900 and 1901 she was temporarily withdrawn from whaling and used as a freighter and passenger ship for the Nome gold rush. In 1908, her whaling service over, she was used as a trading and freighting vessel; her auxiliary plant was removed before 1916, and she sailed thereafter as a barkentine. About 1920 she was renamed *Kamchatka,* rerigged as a schooner, and entered the Siberian trade from Seattle. In 1921, she burned and sank off the Aleutians.

MANUSCRIPT ACCOUNTS:
Voyage of 1885: incomplete journal kept by G. F. Bauldry (SCS). *Voyage of 1896*: logbook kept by W. F. Macomber, first mate (BLHU). *Voyage of 1898*: journal kept by G. B. Leavitt (BLHU).

Thrasher at San Francisco, about 1890
photograph courtesy of San Francisco Maritime Museum

Thrasher in 1916
Old Dartmouth Historical Society

Kamchatka, formerly *Thrasher*, at Seattle, 1920
Old Dartmouth Historical Society

William Lewis at San Francisco, about 1890
photograph courtesy of San Francisco Maritime Museum
William Baylies, before her conversion to steam power, is in
the distance.

WILLIAM LEWIS

TONNAGE: 463
DIMENSIONS: 134' x 30' x 16.5'
RIG: bark
HORSEPOWER: nominal 250 (estimated)

Built at Bath by the Kelley, Spear Company, successor to
Goss, Sawyer & Packard, *William Lewis* was launched in
1888. In 1891, after completing three Arctic voyages, she
was lost when her captain, Albert C. Sherman, in the
autumnal half-light of late September mistook the snow-
covered sandspit at Point Barrow for a strip of slush ice and
ran her hard aground. Crew and cargo were taken out
aboard *Navarch*. The hulk was accidentally burned in
March 1892 by salvagers.

89

Alexander at Cape Prince of Wales, Alaska, 1903
Old Dartmouth Historical Society

ALEXANDER

TONNAGE: 294

DIMENSIONS: 158′ x 26′ x 13′

RIG: bark

HORSEPOWER: 500

Built in New York in 1855, *Alexander* first bore the name *S. S. Astoria.* After a period of Russian ownership, during which she was known as S. S. *Alexander,* she returned to the United States to serve H. Liebes & Company, furriers of San Francisco. Between 1894 and 1905, she made ten Arctic whaling voyages, wintering on three of them. On August 12, 1906, when cruising under sail and steam in fog, she went ashore at Cape Parry. The crew, believing no vessels planned to winter in the Arctic that year, abandoned her and sailed in whaleboats 360 miles to Herschel Island. Arriving at Pauline Cove in a gale, they found the *Charles Hanson,* delayed from departing by poor weather, and left the Arctic aboard her.

MANUSCRIPT ACCOUNTS:

Voyage of 1897: logbook kept by W. S. Varnum, first mate (ODHS). *Voyage of 1898*: logbook kept by W. S. Varnum, first mate (ODHS). *Voyage of 1899*: logbook kept by W. S. Varnum, first mate (ODHS). *Voyage of 1900*: logbook kept by W. S. Varnum, first mate (ODHS). *Voyage of 1901*: logbook kept by T. F. Mulligan, first mate (ODHS). *Voyage of 1902*: logbook kept by T. F. Mulligan, first mate (ODHS);

journal kept by J. A. Tilton, master (DCHS). *Voyage of 1903*: logbook kept by T. F. Mulligan, first mate (ODHS); journal kept by J. A. Tilton, master (DCHS). *Voyage of 1904*: incomplete logbook kept by T. F. Mulligan, first mate (ODHS); journal kept by J. A. Tilton, master (DCHS). *Voyage of 1905-1906*: journal kept by J. A. Tilton, master (DCHS).

Alexander at Cape Parry, 1910
photograph courtesy of the American Museum of Natural History

ALLIANCE

TONNAGE: 271
DIMENSIONS: 125′ x 27′ x 12′
RIG: unknown
HORSEPOWER: unknown

In 1885 and 1886, *Alliance* made whaling voyages to the Arctic from San Francisco. She was built in Astoria, Oregon, but her career is otherwise obscure.

Not illustrated

Bowhead (II) (right) and *Beluga* (left), Oakland Estuary
photograph courtesy of San Francisco Maritime Museum

BOWHEAD (II)

TONNAGE: 381

DIMENSIONS: 133.5′ x 23.5′ x 16.1′

RIG: bark

HORSEPOWER: 265

Bowhead, formerly *Haardraade,* was built at Christiana, Norway, in 1871. In 1897, she was purchased by Captain John A. Cook, who sailed her to the Arctic by way of the Suez Canal in time for the season of 1898. *Bowhead* made seven Arctic voyages, first under Norwegian registry, then Chilean, finally American. She left the whaling trade after the 1908 season and was sold in 1915 to a movie company to be used as a target for torpedoes. Despite the damage inflicted to the old vessel, she refused to sink, and had to be towed to the California shore and burned.

MANUSCRIPT ACCOUNTS:

Voyage of 1903-1906: journal kept by J. A. Tilton, relief master (DCHS); incomplete engineer's logbook kept by R. B. Spencer, chief engineer (NHA). *Voyage of 1908*: logbook kept by T. F. Mulligan, first mate (DCHS).

Fearless flying the Nicaraguan flag at Pitt Point, Alaska, 1898
photograph courtesy of the Peabody Museum of Salem

FEARLESS

TONNAGE: 220

DIMENSIONS: 157.1' x 33.3' x 18.3'

RIG: bark

HORSEPOWER: unknown

Captain James McKenna purchased *Fearless*, formerly *Elida*, in Norway in 1893, and took her on three Arctic whaling voyages between 1894 and 1901, sailing under Nicaraguan registry. She was lost at Dutch Harbor in the Aleutians in November 1901, while returning from her third voyage.

Grampus, 1887
photograph courtesy of New Bedford Free Public Library

GRAMPUS

TONNAGE: 326
DIMENSIONS: 135′ x 21.5′ x 14.5′
RIG: barkentine
HORSEPOWER: 30

Formerly the U.S. revenue cutter *Richard Rush, Grampus* was bought by the Pacific Steam Whaling Company and refitted for whaling, sailing on the first of her nine Arctic voyages in 1886. She wintered in the Arctic on four voyages. With the *Mary D. Hume* and *Nicoline,* she was in the first group to winter at Herschel Island. Fatally nipped in the ice near Point Barrow on July 18, 1901, she was beached and condemned there.

MANUSCRIPT ACCOUNT:

Voyage of 1899-1900: journal kept by G. B. Leavitt, master (BLHU).

Jeanette at San Francisco
photograph courtesy of Peabody Museum of Salem

JEANETTE

TONNAGE: 290

DIMENSIONS: 116' x 27.2' x 13.2'

RIG: brigantine

HORSEPOWER: 120

Although built for the Arctic whale fishery, *Jeanette* differed significantly from the class of steam whalers. She was constructed in 1892 at Benicia, California, and sent north by Roth, Blum & Company to take part in the exploitation of the rich whaling grounds near Herschel Island. By this time the price of oil had fallen so low that little effort was expended in taking it; consequently large vessels, more expensive to operate, were not required for the fishery.

From 1893 to 1911, *Jeanette* made sixteen Arctic voyages and wintered on three of them. As the bowhead stocks became depleted toward the end of the century, whaling vessels were forced to travel farther in search of them. In 1899, *Jeanette* is reported to have sailed along the west and north coasts of Banks Island, the first vessel to have done so in nearly fifty years. After the 1909 season, she was stripped of her engine and used primarily to carry freight to the Arctic. Her last northern voyage was probably made in 1914.

Jesse H. Freeman before her conversion to a bark
photograph courtesy of the Society for the Preservation of New England Antiquities

JESSE H. FREEMAN

TONNAGE: 516

DIMENSIONS: 146.2′ x 30.1′ x 17.4′

RIG: bark

HORSEPOWER: 300?

Originally a steam schooner in the banana trade, *Jesse H. Freeman* was built in 1883 at Bath by Goss, Sawyer & Packard. She was altered to a bark rig, probably in 1887 or 1888, then sailed on seven whaling voyages for the Pacific Steam Whaling Company from 1888 to 1897, going to the Arctic six times and to the Japan and Okhotsk grounds once. On her last voyage from 1894 to 1897 she wintered in the Arctic twice but was caught by ice after rounding Point Barrow, bound for home. Her crew escaped to *Orca,* which was crushed in turn, and both crews found temporary shelter aboard *Belvedere* before walking to Point Barrow to spend the winter in hastily-repaired quarters.

MANUSCRIPT ACCOUNT:

Voyage of 1890-1891: incomplete journal kept by J. A. Cook, master (KWM).

Karluk at Seattle, 1913
photograph courtesy of the Public Archives of Canada

KARLUK

TONNAGE: 321
DIMENSIONS: 125.6′ x 27′ x 14.2′
RIG: brigantine
HORSEPOWER: 150

Karluk was launched at Benicia, California, in 1884 to participate in the Alaskan salmon trade and was bought by Roth, Blum & Company in 1892 to operate on the newly-opened whaling grounds near Herschel Island. She made fourteen voyages to the Arctic, wintering on five of them. In 1910, after her thirteenth voyage, she was bought by Stabens & Friedman, a San Francisco outfitting firm, which operated her in the season of 1911, then withdrew her from the fishery. She was idle until 1913 when she was purchased by Vilhjalmur Stefansson and refitted at Esquimault, British Columbia, for service as the main ship of the Canadian Arctic Expedition. On her way to Amundsen Gulf in the summer of that year, she was caught in the ice near Cape Halkett, Alaska. Strong currents eventually carried the frozen-in vessel to Wrangel Island, where she was crushed in mid-winter. Several of her crew died on the trek across the ice to the Island, but others reached it safely and remained there until their rescue the following summer.

MANUSCRIPT ACCOUNTS:
Voyage of 1904-1906: logbook (PPL); incomplete engineer's journal kept by W. Godbeer, chief engineer (PPL).

Lucretia fitting out at New Bedford for her maiden voyage, 1877
photograph courtesy of The Mariners Museum (Albert M. Barnes Collection)

LUCRETIA

TONNAGE: 317, later 350
DIMENSIONS: 115′ x 27.4′ x 16.6′
RIG: bark
HORSEPOWER: unknown

Lucretia, the first of the vessels converted to steam-auxiliary power for use in the Pacific Arctic fishery, was built at Bath in 1877 and sailed on one whaling voyage before William Lewis arranged to have her powered in 1881. She left New Bedford for the Arctic on October 1 of that year but encountered a severe storm and lost her topmasts, bowsprit, many spars and all but one of her boats. Rather than endure a slow refit at a foreign port, *Lucretia* returned to New Bedford and left again on December 14. She continued to be plagued by bad luck, as heavy gales prevented her from rounding Cape Horn and forced her captain to take her to the Pacific by way of the Cape of Good Hope and the Indian Ocean. She arrived in San Francisco in November 1882 having missed the Arctic season and having taken only thirty barrels of sperm oil in more than a year.

Lucretia made seven Arctic voyages from San Francisco. In 1883, when her crew mutinied in the Bering Sea, Captain Edmund Kelley supressed the insurrection by shooting and killing the leader. *Lucretia* was lost on September 5, 1889, on a shoal at the northwest point of Herald Island.

MANUSCRIPT ACCOUNTS:

Voyage of 1881: journal kept by I. H. Reynolds, chief engineer (MSI); logbook (ODHS). *Voyage of 1881-1882*: journal kept by I. H. Reynolds, chief engineer (MSI); logbook (ODHS). *Voyage of 1882-1883*: logbook kept by H. B. Chace, first mate (ODHS). *Voyage of 1883-1884*: logbook (ODHS). *Voyage of 1884-1885*: logbook (ODHS).

Mary D. Hume at Herschel Island in the 1890's
Old Dartmouth Historical Society

Mary D. Hume at Seattle, 1974
photograph by John R. Bockstoce

MARY D. HUME

TONNAGE: 164.78

DIMENSIONS: 98.2′ x 23′ x 10′

RIG: brigantine

HORSEPOWER: 240

Mary D. Hume, the smallest of the steam whalers, was perhaps the most famous. Designed as a coastal freighter and tow boat, she was launched on January 20, 1881, at Ellenburgh, Oregon, as a schooner-rigged auxiliary steamer. Although too small to carry tryworks, she was bought by the Pacific Steam Whaling Company in 1889 for use in their experiment of wintering at Herschel Island.

Her first voyage began inauspiciously. During a hasty outfitting, she was rerigged as a brigantine. The careless workmanship was exposed by a gale south of the Aleutians when she lost her main- and fore-topmasts. At Unalaska her main-topmast was replaced by a whaleboat's mast, which was sufficient only to hold a lookout and set signals on, but was incapable of carrying a gaff topsail. *Mary D. Hume,* nonetheless, proceeded to set records on each of her two whaling voyages. On the first, she returned having taken thirty-seven whales, a catch valued at $400,000. The second lasted nearly six-and-a-half years and is among the longest recorded whaling voyages in American history. During it, the Pacific Steam Whaling Company maintained the vessel at Herschel, sending up fresh crewmen, supplies, and Captain

George B. Leavitt, who replaced William Hegarty after three Arctic winters.

On *Mary D. Hume*'s return from the Arctic in 1899, she again encountered a wild storm south of the Aleutians. Her four boats were lost, hatches were torn off, and leaking caused the engine to go dead. As the little vessel began to yaw, the mainmast snapped, and two of her crewmen were lost overboard.

Mary D. Hume is the last of the Arctic steam whalers still afloat and holds the distinction of being the only vessel from the historic American whaling industry still in commercial service. Today, her hull ninety-five years old, she works as a tug in Puget Sound.

MANUSCRIPT ACCOUNT:

Voyage of 1893-1899: incomplete journal kept by G. B. Leavitt, master (BLHU).

Herman in 1917
photograph courtesy of the California Academy of Sciences

MORNING STAR, later HERMAN

TONNAGE: 471, later 410
DIMENSIONS: 131.3′ x 29.9′ x 12.2′
RIG: barkentine, later schooner
HORSEPOWER: 100, later unknown

Herman, formerly the missionary steam barkentine *Morning Star,* was built at Bath in 1884. In 1903, she was acquired by H. Liebes & Company of San Francisco and sailed on one Arctic voyage before being refitted and renamed for Herman Liebes. On her second voyage, lasting from 1904 to 1906, she wintered twice in the north; thereafter she made annual trips, with the probable exception of 1908, until withdrawn from service after the season of 1924. She posted no returns of whale products after 1913, and although clearing port as a whaler, she engaged primarily in trading and freighting. In 1916 she was rerigged as a three-masted schooner and fitted with a semi-diesel engine.

MANUSCRIPT ACCOUNTS:

Voyage of 1914: logbook (CAS). *Voyage of 1917:* journal kept by A. Liebes, purser (CAS).

Herman at Banks Island, 1914
photograph courtesy of Bernhard Kilian

Newport at Pitt Point, Alaska, 1898
Old Dartmouth Historical Society

NEWPORT

TONNAGE: 281.42

DIMENSIONS: 133.5' x 25.5' x 9.9'

RIG: barkentine

HORSEPOWER: nominal 65

Newport was built in 1875 at San Francisco and served as a coasting steamer before entering the whale fishery. She was fitted out by the Pacific Steam Whaling Company in 1892 for her only whaling voyage, which lasted until 1898 and ranks second to *Mary D. Hume* among the longest whaling voyages in American history. Like the *Hume, Newport* was used as an Arctic-based catcher ship, annually resupplied and re-staffed by the Company.

MANUSCRIPT ACCOUNT:

Voyage of 1892-1898: incomplete journal kept by G. B. Leavitt, master (BLHU).

William Baylies
Private collection

WILLIAM BAYLIES

TONNAGE: 380

DIMENSIONS: 118.5' x 28' x 16.5'

RIG: bark

HORSEPOWER: unknown

William Baylies was launched at Bath in 1886 and made six Arctic whaling voyages under sail from San Francisco before being converted to steam-auxiliary power in 1894. Fourteen more northern voyages followed until June 1908, when she was crushed by ice in Anadyr Gulf.

MANUSCRIPT ACCOUNTS:

Voyage of 1886-1887: logbook (PPL). *Voyage of 1887-1888*: logbook (PPL). *Voyage of 1888-1889*: logbook (PPL). *Voyage of 1889-1890*: logbook (PPL). *Voyage of 1890-1891*: logbook (PPL). *Voyage of 1891-1892*: logbook (PPL). *Voyage of 1892-1893*: logbook (ODHS). *Voyage of 1894-1895*: logbook (ODHS); journal (PPL). *Voyage of 1896*: logbook kept by S. P. Smith, first mate (ODHS). *Voyage of 1899*: incomplete logbook, kept by S. F. Cottle, first mate (ODHS). *Voyage of 1900*: logbook kept by G. F. Tilton, first mate (ODHS). *Voyage of 1901*: logbook kept by G. F. Tilton, first mate (ODHS). *Voyage of 1906*: logbook (KWM). *Voyage of 1907*: logbook (KWM).

Barbara Hernster
photograph courtesy of San Francisco Maritime Museum

BARBARA HERNSTER

TONNAGE: 148
DIMENSIONS: 102.3' x 29.7' x 8.3'
RIG: schooner
HORSEPOWER: 85

The only recorded voyage of the gasoline centerboard schooner *Barbara Hernster* took place in 1904. The vessel had been built at Fairhaven, California, in 1887 and converted to a gasoline auxiliary in 1901. It was probably the success of *Monterey* in the 1903 season that prompted her owner, the Northwest Commercial Company, to outfit her for whaling. After her return to Seattle with 8500 pounds of baleen, she was apparently withdrawn from the fishery and was wrecked in the Bering Sea in 1905.

Charles Hanson as a freighting vessel
photograph courtesy of San Francisco Maritime Museum

CHARLES HANSON

TONNAGE: 192
DIMENSIONS: 107.5' x 30.1' x 8.8'
RIG: schooner
HORSEPOWER: unknown

Built in 1881 at Eureka, California, *Charles Hanson* was
converted to a gasoline auxiliary before 1904, the year of
the first of her two Arctic voyages. On her second voyage
from 1905 to 1906, she was trapped by the ice and forced to
winter east of the Mackenzie River Delta. She returned to
merchant service in 1906 and was later lost in Mexican
waters when her cargo of dynamite exploded.

Elvira
photograph courtesy of San Francisco Maritime Museum

ELVIRA

TONNAGE: 109
DIMENSIONS: 86' x 22.3' x 9.9'
RIG: schooner
HORSEPOWER: unknown

Formerly a Japanese sealer and trader, *Elvira* was built in Misato, Japan. Under Captain C. T. Pedersen she made the first of her two whaling voyages in 1912. On her second voyage she bent her shaft and propeller near Herschel Island and was taken in tow by *Polar Bear* in an effort to escape the heavy ice. The two vessels, however, along with *Belvedere,* were trapped near Barter Island and forced to winter there. With the aid of their engines, *Belvedere* and *Polar Bear* were able to work their way into relative safety behind heavily grounded ice floes, but *Elvira,* her engine useless, remained to seaward of the grounded ice and was lost in an autumn gale. Her crew, fully realizing their dangerous situation, had left the ship and wintered aboard *Belvedere.* Electing to do otherwise, Captain Pedersen walked four hundred miles to Fairbanks, Alaska, then traveled to San Francisco to take charge of *Herman* for the 1914 season.

Left to right: *Belvedere, Elvira,* and *Polar Bear* near Barter Island, Alaska, 1913
Private collection

Monterey
photograph courtesy of the Peabody Museum of Salem

MONTEREY

TONNAGE: 126
DIMENSIONS: 96.5' x 28' x 7.5'
RIG: schooner
HORSEPOWER: unknown

Monterey was the first of the San Francisco Arctic whalers equipped with an internal-combustion engine. She was built at Benicia, California, in 1887 and was variously employed until 1903, when a small gasoline engine was installed in her for her first whaling voyage. Its success encouraged her owners to install a larger engine and with it she made three more voyages from San Francisco before being withdrawn after the 1906 season.

MANUSCRIPT ACCOUNT:
Voyage of 1905: logbook (PPL).

Olga at Nome, 1909
photograph courtesy of San Francisco Maritime Museum

OLGA

TONNAGE: 46
DIMENSIONS: 63.5′ x 20′ x 7′
RIG: schooner
HORSEPOWER: unknown

Olga was built at Benicia, California, in 1890 and was used as a sea-otter hunter before being bought by Captain James McKenna for the whale fishery. She probably wintered twice at Herschel Island on her first whaling voyage from 1901 to 1903, then was converted to a gasoline auxiliary at Dutch Harbor early in 1905. The following summer she cruised in the eastern Beaufort Sea in the care of her cook, Christian Klengenberg, and in company with her owner, McKenna, who was aboard *Charles Hanson*. The two vessels became separated in a fog east of Herschel Island, whereupon Klengenberg wintered *Olga* on the coast of Victoria Island. There, it became the first vessel in many years to trade with the Copper or "Blond" Eskimos. On *Olga*'s return to Herschel in 1906 it was learned that three of the crew had died during the winter. Klengenberg, charged with murdering the men, was subsequently tried and acquitted.

In the autumn of 1906, *Olga* was frozen in near Point Barrow and McKenna sold her to Captain William Mogg. Mogg returned with her to Victoria Island to spend the winter of 1907-1908 and trade with Eskimos. The next sum-

mer, on the way out of the Arctic, *Olga* went aground near Cape Halkett and was again frozen in. Mogg finally got his vessel as far as Nome by the autumn of 1909, only to lose her there in a strong gale.

Polar Bear at Seattle, 1914
photograph courtesy of Bernhard Kilian

POLAR BEAR

TONNAGE: 81
DIMENSIONS: 76′ x 20.6′ x 10′
RIG: schooner
HORSEPOWER: 75 (indicated)

Polar Bear was built in 1911 by the E. W. Heath Company of Seattle for Captain Louis Lane and associates. She was modeled after Gloucester fishing schooners and fitted with a three-cylinder gasoline engine. After two trading voyages from Seattle to the Siberian Arctic, *Polar Bear* was fitted out in 1913 for a whaling voyage. Forced to winter near Barter Island with *Elvira* and *Belvedere,* she continued her voyages the next summer.

In 1915, while on her second whaling voyage, *Polar Bear* was sold to Vilhjalmur Stefansson for the Canadian Arctic Expedition. Returning from the expedition in 1918, she again went into the Siberian trade and was stranded and abandoned in the Kolyma River Delta in 1928.

Polar Bear at Banks Island, 1914
Old Dartmouth Historical Society

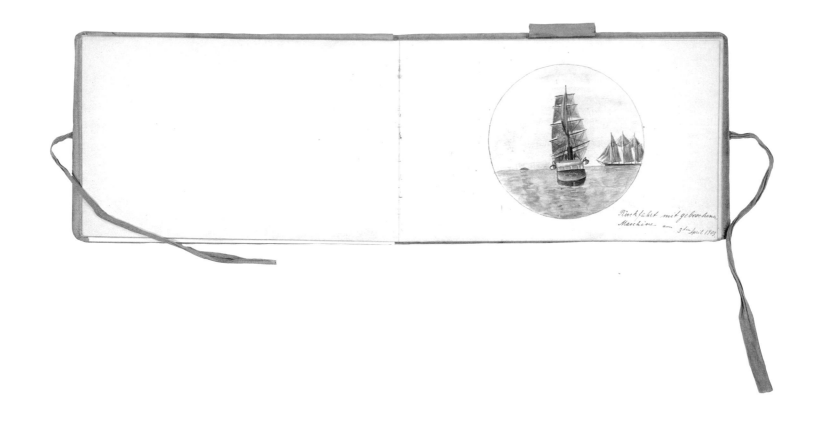

Sketchbook of Alfred Gabali, voyage of the *Bowhead* (II),
1903-1904
*Old Dartmouth Historical Society (Charles F. Batchelder
Collection)*

A Chronological List
of Commercial Wintering Voyages, 1850-1910

John R. Bockstoce and Charles F. Batchelder*

Commercial wintering voyages in the western Arctic were undertaken for three reasons: to trade with the natives for furs, baleen, and ivory; to engage in shore-based spring whaling; and—after 1890—to be nearer the summer feeding grounds of the bowhead whale. For larger vessels, suitable wintering sites were few. Plover (Provideniya) Bay and St. Lawrence (Lavrentiya) Bay in Siberia and Port Clarence, Alaska, were the only good areas in the Bering Strait region that had deep water, safety from moving ice, early break-up, and a substantial native population. The next good harbor, a thousand nautical miles away, was Pauline Cove at Herschel Island in the Yukon Territory. Between Herschel and the harbors of the Bering Strait region, only Elson Lagoon and Peard Bay near Point Barrow could serve in emergencies; both were shallow and had tortuous entrance passages.

After 1895, when the declining numbers of bowheads forced the whalers to range eastward beyond Herschel Island, winterings were carried out less successfully at Baillie Islands near Cape Bathurst, Langton Bay in Franklin Bay and Balaena Bay at Cape Parry. Other than these, the alternative for larger vessels was to anchor on the open coast and to face—often disastrously—the drifting ice. Smaller vessels, drawing less than nine feet, were able to use other sites, such as Marryatt Inlet at Point Hope, Kasegaluk Lagoon at Icy Cape and a number of bays and lagoons on the shores of the Beaufort Sea and Amundsen Gulf.

Unless noted in the remarks column, all vessels were registered at or sailed from San Francisco.

* Mr. Batchelder, a lifelong student of the American whaling industry, prepared an original list of post-1889 wintering voyages in the Beaufort Sea before his death in 1973. Additional voyages, particularly of trading vessels, and further details have been added.

VESSEL	RIG	MASTER	LOCATION	REMARKS
			1850-1851	
Swallow	brig		St. Lawrence Bay, Siberia	Port: Hong Kong; unconfirmed wintering by a trading vessel, lost on return voyage
			1859-1860	
Wailua	brig	Larsen	Plover Bay, Siberia	Port: Hawaii
			1861-1862	
Coral	bark	B. H. Sisson	Plover Bay, Siberia	Port: New Bedford
			1862-1863	
Kohola	brig	Brummerhoff	St. Lawrence Bay, Siberia	Port: Hawaii; Captain killed by natives
Zoe	bark	Simmons	Probably in Bering Strait region	Port: Hawaii
			1869-1870	
Hallie Jackson	schooner	Chapman	Plover Bay, Siberia	Trading vessel
			1870-1871	
Hannah B. Bourne	schooner	Chapman	Plover Bay, Siberia	Trading vessel, abandoned in spring
			1887-1888	
Spy	sloop		Cape Smyth, Alaska	Port not known; wintered on shore
			1888-1889	
Spy	sloop		Cape Smyth, Alaska	Port not known; wintered on shore
	whaleboat	Joseph Tuckfield	Mackenzie Bay, Canada	Port: Point Barrow; wintered on shore; reported Mackenzie Bay whaling grounds

VESSEL	RIG	MASTER	LOCATION	REMARKS

1889-1890

VESSEL	RIG	MASTER	LOCATION	REMARKS
Nicoline	schooner	Louis N. Herendeen	Dease Inlet, Alaska	Unable to reach Herschel Island
Spy	sloop		Cape Smyth, Alaska	Port not known; wintered on shore

1890-1891

VESSEL	RIG	MASTER	LOCATION	REMARKS
Grampus	steam bark	H. H. Norwood	Herschel Island	
Mary D. Hume	steam brigantine	James A. Tilton	Herschel Island	
Nicoline	schooner	Louis N. Herendeen	Herschel Island	
Silver Wave	schooner	Peter Bayne	Sea Horse Islands, Alaska	Grounded and frozen in

1891-1892

VESSEL	RIG	MASTER	LOCATION	REMARKS
Mary D. Hume	steam brigantine	James A. Tilton	Herschel Island	
Silver Wave	schooner	Peter Bayne	Kasegaluk Lagoon, Icy Cape, Alaska	

1892-1893

VESSEL	RIG	MASTER	LOCATION	REMARKS
Balaena	steam bark	H. H. Norwood	Herschel Island	
Grampus	steam bark	Ward P. Vincent	Herschel Island	
Narwhal	steam bark	Horace P. Smith	Herschel Island	
Newport	steam barkentine	W. P. S. Porter	Herschel Island	
Nicoline	schooner	B. F. Tilton	Marryatt Inlet, Point Hope, Alaska	
Silver Wave	schooner	James McKenna	Grantley Harbor, Port Clarence, Alaska	Probably under a caretaker

1893-1894

VESSEL	RIG	MASTER	LOCATION	REMARKS
Balaena	steam bark	H. H. Norwood	Herschel Island	
Emily Schroeder	schooner	Peter Bayne	Marryatt Inlet, Point Hope, Alaska	Damaged and grounded in storm October, 1893
Grampus	schooner	Ward P. Vincent	Herschel Island	
Jeanette	steam brigantine	Edwin W. Newth	Herschel Island	
Karluk	steam brigantine	J. A. Wing	Herschel Island	

VESSEL	RIG	MASTER	LOCATION	REMARKS
La Ninfa	schooner	W. J. Robinson	Probably Marryatt Inlet, Point Hope, Alaska	
Mary D. Hume	steam brigantine	George B. Leavitt	Herschel Island	
Narwhal	steam bark	Horace P. Smith	Herschel Island	
Newport	steam barkentine	James A. Tilton	Herschel Island	
Nicoline	schooner	B. F. Tilton	Marryatt Inlet, Point Hope, Alaska	
Silver Wave	schooner	Collingham	Marryatt Inlet, Point Hope, Alaska	Damaged and grounded in storm October 1893

1894-1895

VESSEL	RIG	MASTER	LOCATION	REMARKS
Alexander	steam bark	F. M. Green	Herschel Island	
Beluga	steam bark	Albert C. Sherman	Herschel Island	
Fearless	steam barkentine	James McKenna	Herschel Island	
Horatio	bark	Eugene B. Penniman	Herschel Island	
Jesse H. Freeman	steam bark	W. P. S. Porter	Herschel Island	
John and Winthrop	bark	A. T. Simmons	Herschel Island	
Mary D. Hume	steam brigantine	George B. Leavitt	Herschel Island	
Navarch	steam bark	John A. Cook	Herschel Island	
Newport	steam barkentine	James A. Tilton	Herschel Island	
Northern Light	bark	Bernard Cogan	Herschel Island	
Rosario	schooner	Edwin Coffin	Herschel Island	
Silver Wave	schooner	Peter Bayne	Marryatt Inlet, Point Hope, Alaska	Aground, abandoned in spring
Thrasher	steam bark	C. E. Weeks	Herschel Island	Captain Weeks killed by fall into hold
Triton	bark	William Hegarty	Herschel Island	
Wanderer	bark	George W. Porter	Herschel Island	
William Baylies	steam bark	John McInnis	Herschel Island	

1895-1896

VESSEL	RIG	MASTER	LOCATION	REMARKS
Alexander	steam bark	F. M. Green	Herschel Island	
Balaena	steam bark	H. H. Williams	Balaena Bay, Cape Parry, Canada	

VESSEL	RIG	MASTER	LOCATION	REMARKS
Beluga	steam bark	Albert C. Sherman	Herschel Island	
Belvedere	steam bark	Joseph A. Whiteside	Herschel Island	
Fearless	steam bark	James McKenna	Herschel Island	
Grampus	steam bark	R. J. Cumiskey	Balaena Bay, Cape Parry, Canada	
Jeanette	steam brigantine	Edwin W. Newth	Herschel Island	
Jesse H. Freeman	steam bark	W. P. S. Porter	Herschel Island	
John and Winthrop	bark	A. T. Simmons	Herschel Island	
Karluk	steam brigantine	J. A. Wing	Herschel Island	
Mary D. Hume	steam brigantine	George B. Leavitt	Herschel Island	
Navarch	steam bark	John A. Cook	Herschel Island	
Newport	steam barkentine	Hartson H. Bodfish	Herschel Island	
Northern Light	bark	John Callaghan	Herschel Island	
Wanderer	bark	George W. Porter	Herschel Island	

1896-1897

VESSEL	RIG	MASTER	LOCATION	REMARKS
Fearless	steam bark	James McKenna	near Shingle Point, Canada	Trapped by ice
Grampus	steam bark	R. J. Cumiskey	Herschel Island	
Jesse H. Freeman	steam bark	W. P. S. Porter	near King Point, Canada	Trapped by ice; captain and half of crew wintered at Herschel Island
Mary D. Hume	steam brigantine	William Hegarty	near Shingle Point, Canada	Trapped by ice
Newport	steam barkentine	George B. Leavitt	Herschel Island	
Wanderer	bark	George W. Porter	Herschel Island	

1897-1898

VESSEL	RIG	MASTER	LOCATION	REMARKS
Balaena	steam bark	H. H. Williams	Langton Bay, Canada	
Beluga	steam bark	Hartson H. Bodfish	Langton Bay, Canada	
Belvedere	steam bark	M. V. B. Millard	Peard Bay, Alaska	Trapped by ice; rescued crews of *Jesse H. Freeman* and *Orca*

VESSEL	RIG	MASTER	LOCATION	REMARKS
Etna	schooner	Christian Klengenberg	Marryatt Inlet, Point Hope, Alaska	Trading and shore whaling
Fearless	steam bark	James McKenna	Pitt Point, Alaska	Trapped by ice
Grampus	steam bark	R. J. Cumiskey	Langton Bay, Canada	
Jeanie	steam schooner	P. H. Mason	Cape Halkett, Alaska	Trapped by ice; tender to Pacific Steam Whaling Company ships
Mary D. Hume	steam brigantine	William Hegarty	Herschel Island	
Narwhal	steam bark	James A. Tilton	Langton Bay, Canada	
Newport	steam brigantine	George B. Leavitt	Pitt Point, Alaska	Trapped by ice
Rosario	schooner	Edwin Coffin	Point Barrow, Alaska	Trapped by ice; crushed July, 1898
Wanderer	bark	George W. Porter	Herschel Island	Blocked by ice near Barter Island, Alaska; forced to return to Herschel Island

1898-1899

VESSEL	RIG	MASTER	LOCATION	REMARKS
Beluga	steam bark	Hartson H. Bodfish	Baillie Islands, Canada	
Mary D. Hume	steam brigantine	William Hegarty	Herschel Island	
—	schooner	Christian Klengenberg	Probably near Cape Seppings, Alaska	Name and port not known; trading and shore whaling

1899-1900

VESSEL	RIG	MASTER	LOCATION	REMARKS
Balaena	steam bark	H. H. Williams	Langton Bay, Canada	
Fearless	steam bark	James McKenna	Baillie Islands, Canada	
Grampus	steam bark	George B. Leavitt	Baillie Islands, Canada	
Helen	schooner	Christian Klengenberg	Elson Lagoon, Point Barrow, Alaska	Port not known; trading and shore whaling
Narwhal	steam bark	R. J. Cumiskey	Baillie Islands, Canada	

1900-1901

VESSEL	RIG	MASTER	LOCATION	REMARKS
Beluga	steam bark	Hartson H. Bodfish	Baillie Islands, Canada	
Bowhead	steam bark	John A. Cook	Baillie Islands, Canada	
Helen	schooner	Christian Klengenberg	Collinson Point, Camden Bay, Alaska	Port not known; lost in autumn gale

VESSEL	RIG	MASTER	LOCATION	REMARKS
Narwhal	steam bark	R. J. Cumiskey	Baillie Islands, Canada	
Penelope	schooner	H. E. Huffman	Baillie Islands, Canada	
Sophia Sutherland	schooner (3 masted)	Murray	Baillie Islands, Canada	Sold to Eskimos; later wrecked in autumn gale

1901-1902

VESSEL	RIG	MASTER	LOCATION	REMARKS
Altair	schooner	William Mogg	Herschel Island	
Olga	schooner	James McKenna		Probably wintered at Herschel Island
Penelope	schooner	H. E. Huffman	Probably at Baillie Islands, Canada	

1902-1903

VESSEL	RIG	MASTER	LOCATION	REMARKS
Narwhal	steam bark	George B. Leavitt	Herschel Island	
Olga	schooner	James McKenna	Herschel Island	Converted to gasoline auxiliary, 1905
Penelope	schooner		Probably at Herschel Island	Sold to Eskimos: probably Kunuk, Kakotak, Ilavinerk, and Tulugak. Crew and cargo transferred to *William Baylies*

1903-1904

VESSEL	RIG	MASTER	LOCATION	REMARKS
Bonanza	schooner	William Mogg	Herschel Island	
Bowhead	steam bark	John A. Cook	Herschel Island	
Narwhal	steam bark	George B. Leavitt	Herschel Island	
Penelope	schooner		Herschel Island	Port not known

1904-1905

VESSEL	RIG	MASTER	LOCATION	REMARKS
Beluga	steam bark	R. J. Cumiskey	Langton Bay, Canada	
Bonanza	schooner	William Mogg	Herschel Island	Wrecked at King Point, autumn, 1905
Bowhead	steam bark	John A. Cook	Herschel Island	
Herman	steam barkentine	W. S. Varnum	Langton Bay, Canada	
Karluk	steam brigantine	A. H. McGregor	Herschel Island	
Kate Smith	schooner			Probably wintered; place not known
Penelope	schooner		Herschel Island	

VESSEL	RIG	MASTER	LOCATION	REMARKS
			1905-1906	
Alexander	steam bark	James A. Tilton	Herschel Island	Trapped by ice
Beluga	steam bark	R. J. Cumiskey	Baillie Islands, Canada	Trapped by ice; intended to winter at Herschel Island
Belvedere	steam bark	S. F. Cottle	Baillie Islands, Canada	Trapped by ice
Bowhead	steam bark	John A. Cook	Herschel Island	Trapped by ice
Charles Hanson	gasoline schooner	James McKenna	Toker Point, Canada	Trapped by ice; probably intended to winter at Herschel Island
Herman	steam barkentine	W. S. Varnum	Baillie Islands, Canada	Trapped by ice; intended to winter at Herschel Island
Jeanette	steam brigantine	Edwin W. Newth	Herschel Island	Trapped by ice
Karluk	steam brigantine	A. H. McGregor	Herschel Island	Trapped by ice
Narwhal	steam bark	George B. Leavitt	Baillie Islands, Canada	Trapped by ice; intended to winter at Herschel Island
Olga	gasoline schooner	Christian Klengenberg, mate	Bell Island, Victoria Island, Canada	
Penelope	schooner		Herschel Island	Port not known
Thrasher	steam bark	William F. Macomber	Herschel Island	Trapped by ice
			1906-1907	
Narwhal	steam bark	George B. Leavitt	Herschel Island	
Olga	gasoline schooner	James McKenna	Elson Lagoon, Point Barrow, Alaska	Under Eskimo caretaker
Penelope	schooner		Probably Herschel Island	Port not known; master probably Christian Sten; lost September 1907 at Shingle Point, Canada
			1907-1908	
Ivy	schooner	Christian Klengenberg	Elson Lagoon, Point Barrow, Alaska	Trading and shore whaling
Karluk	steam brigantine	J. A. Wing	Herschel Island	
Olga	gasoline schooner	William Mogg	Walker Bay, Victoria Island, Canada	

VESSEL	RIG	MASTER	LOCATION	REMARKS
			1908-1909	
Challenge	schooner	C. T. Pedersen	Elson Lagoon, Point Barrow, Alaska	
Ivy	schooner	Christian Klengenberg	Point Barrow, Alaska	Lost in ice in winter
Olga	gasoline schooner	William Mogg	Cape Halkett, Alaska	Grounded and frozen in; wrecked autumn, 1909 at Nome, Alaska
Rosie H.	schooner	Fritz Wolki	Flaxman Island, Alaska	
			1909-1910	
Argo	gasoline yawl	Ernest deK. Leffingwell	Flaxman Island, Alaska	Port: Seattle; exploring and shore whaling
Homely Hippopotamus	scow	Christian Klengenberg	Baillie Islands, Canada	Port not known
Karluk	steam brigantine	S. F. Cottle	Baillie Islands, Canada	
Rosie H.	schooner	Fritz Wolki	Booth Islands, Cape Parry, Canada	
Teddy Bear	schooner	Joseph Bernard	Barter Island, Alaska	Port: Seattle; trading vessel

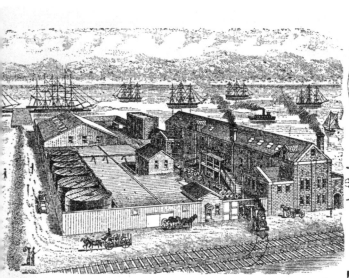

OL SCOURING AND
STEAM LAUNDRY SOAPS.

J.N. KNOWLES.
MANAGER.

EDWIN.L GRIFFITH.
SECRETARY.

ARCTIC OIL WORKS

MANUFACTURERS OF

SPERM WHALE, ELEPHANT & FISH OILS & SOAPS.

Lard and Tallow Oils.

MINERAL, LUBRICATING and ILLUMINATING OILS.

MARINE OILS A SPECIALTY.

OFFICE 28 CALIFORNIA STREET.

SAN FRANCISCO.

Annual Reports of the Chamber of Commerce of San Francisco, 1893-1906.

Baker, William Avery. *A Maritime History of Bath, Maine and the Kennebec River Region.* 2 vols. Bath, Maine: Marine Research Society of Bath, 1973.

Bertonccini, John. "Survivors of the Whaler *Bonanza.*" MS. Old Dartmouth Historical Society, New Bedford, Mass.

Bockstoce, John. "Contacts Between American Whalemen and the Copper Eskimos." *Arctic,* vol. 28, no. 4 (December 1975), 298-299.

————. "The Arctic Whaling Disaster of 1897." *Prologue; The Journal of the National Archives,* vol. 9, no. 1 (March 1977).

Bodfish, Hartson H. *Chasing the Bowhead.* Cambridge, Mass.: Harvard University Press, 1936.

————. "A Letter Home from Herschel Island—1891." *Dukes County Intelligencer,* vol. 8, no. 3 (February 1967), 57-70.

Borden, Gilbert. MS journal, 15 August 1889-23 August 1893. Beinecke Rare Book and Manuscript Library, Yale University.

Brandt, George E. "Frozen Toes but not Cold Feet." U.S. Naval Institute *Proceedings,* vol. 55 (1929), 118-120.

Brower, Charles D. "The Northernmost American: an Autobiography." Updated typescript. U.S. Naval Arctic Research Laboratory, Point Barrow, Alaska.

Brown, James Templeman. "The Whalemen, Vessels and Boats, Apparatus and Methods of the Whale Fishery." In *The Fisheries and Fishery Industries of the United States,* section 5, vol. 2, 218-293. Washington, D.C.: Government Printing Office, 1887.

Chapelle, Howard I. *The National Watercraft Collection.* U.S. National Museum Bulletin No. 219. Washington, D.C.: U.S. National Museum, 1960.

————. "The Development and Design of Arctic Whaling and Sealing Vessels." MS. Stefansson Collection, Dartmouth College.

Collins, J. W. *Report on the Fisheries of the Pacific Coast of the United States.* Washington, D.C.: Government Printing Office, 1891.

Cook, John A. *Pursuing the Whale; A Quarter-Century of Whaling in the Arctic.* Boston and New York: Houghton Mifflin Company, 1926.

Faber, Kurt. *Unter Eskimos und Walfischfängern; Eismeerfarten eines jungen Deutschen.* Stuttgart: Robert Lutz, 1916.

Godsell, Philip H. "Pirate Days in Arctic Waters." *Forest and Outdoors,* vol. 37 (1941), 145-146, 152-153.

Goode, George Brown. *The Fisheries and Fishery Industries of the United States.* Section 5, vol. 2. Washington, D.C.: Government Printing Office, 1887.

Hare, Lloyd C. M. *Salted Tories; The Story of the Whaling Fleet of San Francisco.* Mystic, Connecticut: Marine Historical Association, 1960.

Harrison, Alfred H. *In Search of a Polar Continent, 1905-1907.* London: Edward Arnold, 1908.

Healy, Michael A. *Report of the Cruise of the Revenue Marine Steamer Corwin in the Arctic Ocean in the Year 1884.* Washington, D.C.: Government Printing Office, 1889.

Hegarty, Reginald B. *Returns of Whaling Vessels Sailing from American Ports, 1876-1928: A Continuation of Alexander Starbuck's "History of the American Whale Fishery."* New Bedford: Old Dartmouth Historical Society, 1959.

Hegemann, P. F. A. "Das Eis und die Strömungsverhältnisse des Beringmeeres, der Beringstrasse und des nördlich davon belegenen Eismeeres." *Annalen der Hydrographie und Maritimen Meteorologie,* vol. 18, no. 11. (1890), 425-35.

Hohman, Elmo P. *The American Whaleman; A Study of Life and Labor in the Whaling Industry.* New York: Longmans, Green and Co., 1928.

Hooper, Calvin L. *Report of the Cruise of the U.S. Revenue Steamer Corwin in the Arctic Ocean.* Treasury Department Document No. 118. Washington, D.C.: Government Printing Office, 1881.

Jackson, Sheldon. "Education in Alaska, 1892-1893." In *Report of the Commissioner of Education for the Year 1892-93,* 1705-1748. Washington, D.C.: Government Printing Office, 1895.

Kugler, Richard C. "The Penetration of the Pacific by American Whalemen in the 19th Century." In *National Maritime Museum Monographs and Reports,* No. 2, 20-27. Greenwich, England: National Maritime Museum, 1971.

Leet, Robert E. "American Whalers in the Western Arctic: 1879-1914." Master's thesis, University of San Francisco, 1974.

Lindeman, Moritz. *Die Gegenwärtige Eismeer-fischerei und der Walfang.* Berlin: Otto Salle, 1899.

Maury, Matthew Fontaine. *Explanations and Directions to Accompany the Wind and Current Charts.* 5th ed. Washington, D.C.: C. Alexander, 1853.

Mjelde, Michael Jay. *Glory of the Seas.* Middletown, Conn.: Wesleyan University Press, 1970.

Page, James. *Ice and Ice Movements in Bering Sea during the Spring Months.* Hydrographic Office Publication No. 116. Washington, D.C.: Hydrographic Office, 1900.

Peake, Frank A. *The Bishop Who Ate His Boots: A Biography of Isaac O. Stringer.* Ottawa: Anglican Church of Canada, 1966.

Poole, Dorothy Cottle. "Vineyard Whalemen in the Arctic." *Dukes County Intelligencer,* vol. 13, no. 1 (August 1971), 1-25.

Ray, Patrick Henry. *Report of the International Polar Expedition to Point Barrow, Alaska.* Washington, D.C.: Government Printing Office, 1885.

Russell, Frank, MS journal, April 26, 1893-August 19, 1894. National Anthropological Archives, Smithsonian Institution.

Scammon, Charles M. *The Marine Mammals of the North-western Coast of North America, Described and Illustrated; Together with an Account of the American Whale-Fishery.* San Francisco: John H. Carmany and Co., 1874.

Simpson, Edward. *Report of Ice and Ice Movements in Bering Sea and the Arctic Basin.* Hydrographic Office Publication No. 92. Washington, D.C.: Hydrographic Office, 1890.

Starbuck, Alexander. *History of the American Whale Fishery from its Earliest Inception to the Year 1876.* Waltham, Mass.: by the Author, 1878.

Stevenson, Charles H. "Whalebone: Its Production and Utilization." Bureau of Fisheries Document No. 626. Washington, D.C.: Government Printing Office, 1907.

Stockton, Charles H. "The Arctic Cruise of the U.S.S. Thetis in the Summer and Autumn of 1889." *National Geographic Magazine,* vol. 2, no. 3 (1890), 171-198.

Stone, Andrew J. "Some Results of a Natural History Journey to Northern British Columbia, Alaska, and the Northwest Territory, in the Interest of the American Museum of Natural History." *Bulletin of the American Museum of Natural History,* vol. 13, no. 5 (1900), 31-62.

————. Letter quoted in "The Musk-oxen of Arctic America and Greenland" by J. A. Allen. *Bulletin of the American Museum of Natural History,* vol. 14 (December 1901), 84-86.

Tower, Walter S. *A History of the American Whale Fishery.* Philadelphia: University of Pennsylvania, 1907.

Tressler, Donald K. *Marine Products of Commerce; Their Acquisition, Handling, Biological Aspects, and the Science and Technology of their Preparation and Preservation.* New York: Chemical Catalogue Company, Inc., 1923.

Whittaker, C. E. *Arctic Eskimo.* London: Seeley, Service & Co., n.d. [1937?].

INDEX OF NAMES